Building Mathematical Thinking

SKINNY CONCEPTS: Book One

Marsha Stanton

 eps

Educators Publishing Service, Inc.
Cambridge and Toronto

Acknowledgements

Thanks to librarian, Mark Piel, and his fine staff at the New York Society Library. There, I enjoyed a quiet work space, free from all distractions. This special sanctuary enabled me to put my ideas together.

Dedication

To Loving Friends who support me with their time, wisdom, creativity, and sensitivity—Toby, Janet, 2 Pennys, 2 Karens, Sarah, Judy, Molly, Teddy, Gail, Carolyn, Millie, Marlene, Gina
I am forever grateful.

Design & Graphics by Rebecca C. Royen
Some images courtesy of Nova Development Corporation

Printed in the USA
ISBN 0-8388-2551-6

Contents

Place Value

example

Draw a ring around groups of 10.

☆ ☆ ☆ ☆ ☆ ☆ ☆ ☆ ☆ ☆   ☆ ☆ ☆ ☆ ☆ ☆ ☆ ☆ ☆ ☆   ☆ ☆ ☆ ☆ ☆ ☆ ☆

There are 2 tens and 7 ones. The number is 27.

⟨ ⟨

_____ tens and _____ ones = _____

△ △ △ △ △ △ △ △ △ △ △ △ △ △ △ △

_____ tens and _____ ones = _____

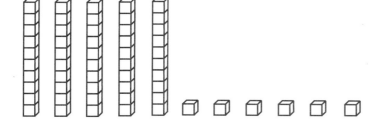

_____ tens and _____ ones = _____

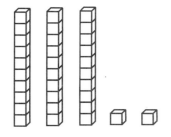

_____ tens and _____ ones = _____

40 + 9 = _____ tens and _____ones   Number: _____

30 + 8 = _____ tens and _____ones   Number: _____

10 + 7 = _____ tens and _____ ones   Number: _____

94 = _____ tens and _____ ones

73 = _____ tens and _____ ones

60 = _____ tens and _____ ones

19 = _____ tens and _____ ones

Draw a picture to show 4 tens and 3 ones. Use x's or the first letter of your name.

examples

Round 8<u>3</u> to the nearest ten.

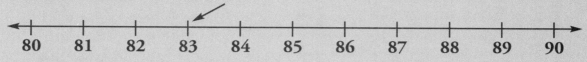

83 is between 80 (8 tens) and 90 (9 tens), but it is nearer to 80.
83 rounds to 80.

Round 3<u>7</u> to the nearest ten.

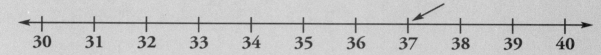

37 is between 30 (3 tens) and 40 (4 tens), but it is nearer to 40.
37 rounds to 40.

Round 2<u>5</u> to the nearest ten.

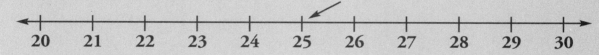

25 is halfway between 20 (2 tens) and 30 (3 tens). When a number is halfway, round to the higher number.
25 rounds to 30.

54 rounded to the nearest ten is _____.   15 rounded to the nearest ten is _____.

68 rounded to the nearest ten is _____.   49 rounded to the nearest ten is _____.

81 rounded to the nearest ten is _____.   22 rounded to the nearest ten is _____.

75 rounded to the nearest ten is _____.   27 rounded to the nearest ten is _____.

My secret for rounding a number to the nearest ten is _____

_____

 List all the 2-digit numbers that round to 40. _____

_____

example

How many hundreds, tens, and ones are in the picture?
What is the number?
Key: ▱ **= 1 one**

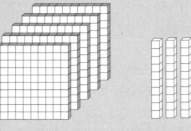

5 hundreds, 3 tens, and 4 ones equal 534.

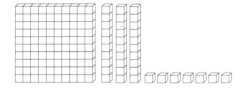

_____ hundreds, _____ tens, and _____ ones = _____

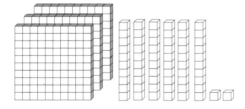

_____ hundreds, _____ tens, and _____ ones = _____

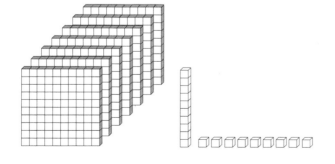

_____ hundreds, _____ tens, and _____ ones = _____

_____ hundreds, _____ tens, and _____ ones = $ _____

_____ hundreds, _____ tens, and _____ ones = $ _____

800 + 30 + 9 = _____ hundreds, _____ tens, and _____ ones = _____

600 + 90 + 4 = _____ hundreds, _____ tens, and _____ ones = _____

500 + 2 = _____ hundreds, _____ tens, and _____ ones = _____

291 = _____ hundreds, _____ tens, and _____ ones

579 = _____ hundreds, _____ tens, and _____ ones

940 = _____ hundreds, _____ tens, and _____ ones

170 = _____ hundreds, _____ tens, and _____ ones

PLACE VALUE

Round 4_7_2 to the nearest hundred.

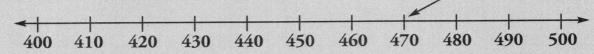

472 is between 400 (4 hundreds) and 500 (5 hundreds), but it is nearer to 500. 472 rounds to 500.

Round 2_3_1 to the nearest hundred.

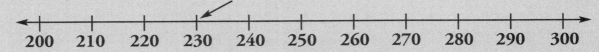

231 is between 200 (2 hundreds) and 300 (3 hundreds), but it is nearer to 200. 231 rounds to 200.

Round 3_5_0 to the nearest hundred.

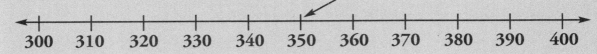

350 is halfway between 300 (3 hundreds) and 400 (4 hundreds). When a number is halfway, you round to the larger number. 350 rounds to 400.

175 _____   293 _____   554 _____   837 _____

696 _____   519 _____   684 _____   112 _____

My secret for rounding to the nearest hundred is _____

_____

 List at least ten 3-digit numbers that round to 700 when they are rounded to the nearest hundred. _____

_____

example

How many thousands, hundreds, tens, and ones are in the picture?
What is the number?

Key: ⬜ = 1 one

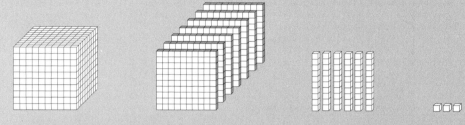

1 thousand, 7 hundreds, 6 tens, and 3 ones equal 1763.

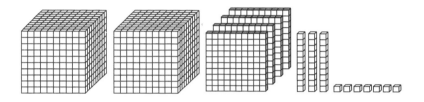

_____ thousands, _____ hundreds, _____ tens, and _____ ones = _____

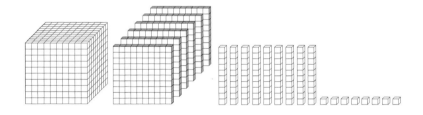

_____ thousands, _____ hundreds, _____ tens, and _____ ones = _____

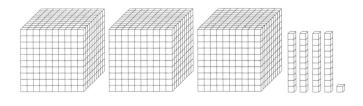

_____ thousands, _____ hundreds, _____ tens, and _____ ones = _____

_____ thousands, _____ hundreds, _____ tens, and _____ ones = $_____

_____ thousands, _____ hundreds, _____ tens, and _____ ones = $_____

9000 + 700 + 60 + 2 = _____ thousands, _____ hundreds, _____ tens, and _____ ones = _____

8000 + 500 + 4 = _____ thousands, _____ hundreds, _____ tens, and _____ ones = _____

2000 + 3 = _____ thousands, _____ hundreds, _____ tens, and _____ ones = _____

7654 = _____ thousands, _____ hundreds, _____ tens, and _____ ones

2078 = _____ thousands, _____ hundreds, _____ tens, and _____ ones

4360 = _____ thousands, _____ hundreds, _____ tens, and _____ ones

809 = _____ thousands, _____ hundreds, _____ tens, and _____ ones

example

Place the comma in 4761.
Count 3 places from the ones, then write the comma.
4,761

four *thousand* seven hundred sixty-one
Write the number seven *thousand* eight hundred twenty-three.
7,823

Place the comma in each of the numbers.

5458   3009   16281

7605   5334   72009

Write the number.

two thousand thirty-five   _____

seventeen thousand nineteen   _____

fifty-one thousand two hundred seventy-eight _____

twelve thousand four hundred sixty-four   _____

seven thousand nine hundred forty-five   _____

four thousand six hundred fifty-two   _____

five thousand three hundred seventy-five   _____

nineteen thousand eighty-eight   _____

example

What is the value of the underlined digit?

9̲87   *9 is in the hundreds place. Its value is* 900.
5,08̲7   *8 is in the tens place. Its value is* 80.
3̲,049   *3 is in the thousands place. Its value is* 3,000.
71̲5   *5 is in the ones place. Its value is* 5.

What is the value of the underlined digit?

6̲74   Its value is _____.

8̲70   Its value is _____.

4̲,031   Its value is _____.

5,67̲8   Its value is _____.

9,3̲04   Its value is _____.

64̲5   Its value is _____.

2,09̲1   Its value is _____.

33̲2   Its value is _____.

6̲,922   Its value is _____.

Which digit has the greater value in 8,649, the 6 or the 9? _____

example

Write 864 in expanded notation.
864 = *800 + 60 + 4*

Write the number in expanded notation.

437 = _____

125 = _____

6,093 = _____

549 = _____

1,138 = _____

720 = _____

8,909 = _____

5,665 = _____

 What number is represented by 400 + 7000 + 3 + 90? _____

PLACE VALUE

example

Find the number that has 4 thousands, 7 hundreds, 3 tens, and 9 ones.
Add the values of each place.
4,000 + 700 + 30 + 9 = 4,739   **or**

$$\begin{array}{r} 4,000 \\ 700 \\ 30 \\ +\ 9 \\ \hline 4,739 \end{array}$$

600 + 20 + 9 = _____   4,000 + 700 + 80 + 8 = _____

1,000 + 40 + 6 = _____   900 + 6 = _____

800 + 50 = _____   5,000 + 700 + 10 + 9 = _____

Complete using >, <, or =.

94 _____ 36
94 is greater than 36. 94 ___>___ 36

851 _____ 1,034
851 is less than 1,034. 851 ___<___ 1,034

352 _____ 300 + 50 + 2
352 is equal to 300 + 50 + 2. 352 ___=___ 300 + 50 + 2

24 _____ 42   603 _____ 630

99 _____ 111   752 _____ 700 + 50 + 2

70 + 9 _____ 60 + 9   447 _____ 400 + 30 + 8

700 + 6 _____ 706   543 _____ 535

9,213 _____ 9,331   2,176 _____ 2,711

Write in order from least to greatest.

643   372   4,081   4,998   634   99

_____   _____

example

Write 76 different ways.

In expanded notation,
76 = 70 + 6 *or* 7 tens and 6 ones.

After renaming 1 ten for 10 ones,
76 = 60 + 16 *or* 6 tens and 16 ones.

After renaming 2 tens for 10 ones,
76 = 50 + 26 *or* 5 tens and 26 ones.

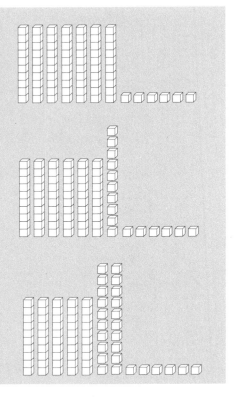

Write each number different ways.

58 = _____   _____   _____

37 = _____   _____   _____

54 = _____   _____   _____

159 = _____   _____   _____

70 = _____   _____   _____

Addition

example

Gail found 6 shells on the beach. Lynn found 9 shells. How many shells did they find in all?

Gail's Shells   Lynn's Shells

Addition Equation: $6 + 9 = 15$
Gail and Lynn found 15 shells in all.

Write the addition equation for joining two sets.

_____

_____

_____

_____

23

example

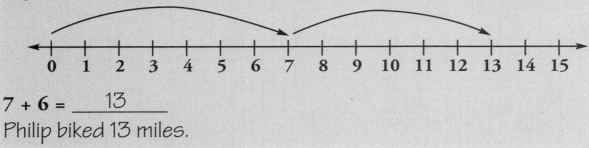

Philip biked for 7 miles. He met his friend Steven and they biked together for 6 more miles. How many miles did Philip bike in all?

7 + 6 = _____13_____

Philip biked 13 miles.

Draw arrows on the number line to find the sum.

8 + 3 = _____

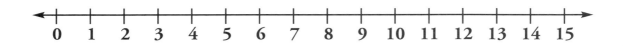

4 + 9 = _____

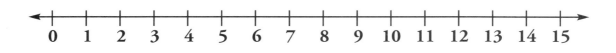

7 + 5 = _____

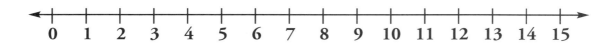

Write the addition equation shown on the number line.

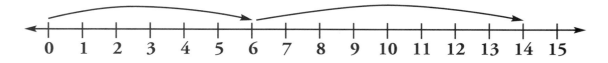

_____ + _____ = _____

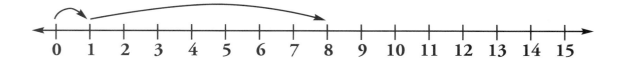

_____

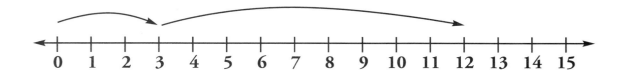

_____

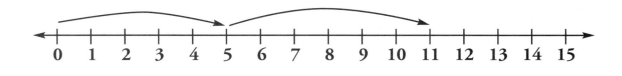

_____

Show the addends to find the sum of 8 + 5.

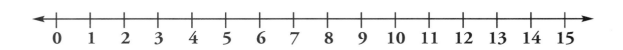

ADDITION

Look at the Addition Table on the next page. The addends are along the side and the top. The sums are inside the table.

Find the sum of 5 on the table. What is the addition equation for 5?

$2 + 3 = 5$

Find the sum of 11 on the table.
Write the addition equation for 11.

_____ + _____ = 11

Find the sum of 8 on the table.
Write the addition equation for 8.

_____ + _____ = 8

Find the addends 6 and 7 on the table.
Write their sum in the correct box.

Complete the table.
Look for patterns and secrets.

What are four patterns and secrets that you found? _____

_____

_____

_____

Addition Table

+	0	1	2	3	4	5	6	7	8	9	10
0											
1											
2				5							
3						8					
4											
5											
6											
7					11						
8											
9											
10											

Commutative Property: Changing the Order of Addends

8 + 4 = _____   4 + 8 = _____

What did you notice? _____

9 + 5 = 5 + _____   7 + 8 = _____ + 7

Look at the Addition Table on page 27. Find 3 more examples of the Commutative Property. List them.

_____

My secret for the Commutative Property is _____

_____

Identity Property: Adding 0 to a Number

6 + 0 = _____   9 + 0 = _____   14 + 0 = _____   0 + 19 = _____

What did you notice? _____

7 + _____ = 7   0 + _____ = 6   _____ + 15 = 15   _____ + 0 = 12

Use the Addition Table on page 000. Find 3 more examples of addition with 0.

_____

My secret for adding 0 to a number is _____

_____

Associative Property: Changing the Grouping of Addends

Get 3 rods: 2, 8, and 9. (If you do not have rods, make a card for each addend.)
Use the rods or cards to show 2 + 8 + 9.

First, group the 2 and 8 together. Find the sum.

$(2 + 8) + 9 =$ _____

Second, change the grouping. Group the 8 and the 9 together. Find the sum.

$2 + (8 + 9) =$ _____

What did you notice? _____

Group the set of numbers 2 ways. Use parentheses ( ) to show the grouping.
Find the sums.

4, 6, 7   _____   _____

3, 5, 8   _____   _____

My secret for the Associative Property is _____

_____

Use your 3 secrets to complete the equations.

$3 + (5 + 7) = (3 + 5) +$ _____ $(4 + 6) + 3 = 4 + ($_____$+ 3)$

$5 +$_____$= 5$ $6 + 4 = 4 +$ _____

   $(7 +$ _____$) + 9 = 7 + 9$

It is helpful to have all the addends for 10 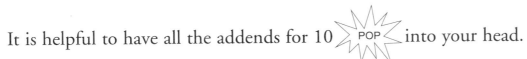 POP into your head.

Fill in the addends across the top of the Addition Table.

Addition Table

+											
0	10										
1		10									
2			10								
3				10							
4					10						
5						10					
6							10				
7								10			
8									10		
9										10	
10											10

Fill in the addend that will sum to 10.

Practice so that these answers POP into your head quickly.

10

1	9
9	
2	
3	
8	
5	
6	
7	
4	
7	
8	

10

5	
8	
6	
7	
1	
9	
3	
2	
8	
4	
5	

10

7	
6	
5	
2	
8	
9	
6	
1	
4	
3	
7	

6 + _____ = 10   7 + _____ = 10   2 + _____ = 10

5 + _____ = 10   9 + _____ =10   _____ + 3 = 10

Find the sum. Look for a secret using addends for 10.

$1 + 2 + 3 + 4 + 5 + 6 + 7 + 8 + 9 =$ _____

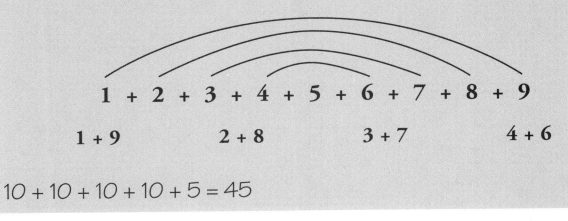

$$1 + 2 + 3 + 4 + 5 + 6 + 7 + 8 + 9$$

$1 + 9$ $2 + 8$ $3 + 7$ $4 + 6$

$10 + 10 + 10 + 10 + 5 = 45$

Show the tens and find the sums.

$9 + 4 + 3 + 1 + 6 + 7 =$ _____

$8 + 2 + 7 + 4 + 3 + 1 + 5 + 5 + 9 =$ _____

$6 + 3 + 2 + 1 + 4 + 7 + 8 + 9 + 8 + 2 + 8 =$ _____

$8 + 3 + 1 + 9 + 5 + 2 + 5 + 7 + 4 =$ _____

$5 + 5 + 4 + 6 + 8 + 1 + 2 + 9 + 9 + 3 + 7 =$ _____

$4 + 1 + 1 + 9 + 5 + 8 + 6 + 5 + 2 + 9 + 3 + 7 + 7 =$ _____

example

Sofia has 3 pet rabbits, Jack has 9, and Desmond has 7. How many rabbits do they have altogether?

3 + 9 + 7 = 19

$$\begin{array}{r} 3 \\ 9 \\ +\ 7 \\ \hline 19 \end{array}$$

They have 19 rabbits altogether.

Look for pairs that add to 10.

8	9	5	6
2	4	5	1
7	6	8	4
3	1	4	3
5	7	9	9
5	4	2	7
+ 9	+ 3	+ 1	+ 8

1 + 7 + 3 + 9 + 2 + 8 = _____   3 + 7 + 9 + 6 + 4 = _____

ADDITION

Latoya bought 60 markers at one store and 20 markers at another store. How many markers did she buy?

Use rods, blocks, or an abacus. Take out 6 tens and 2 tens.

6 tens + 2 tens = 8 tens   **or**   **60 + 20 =** 80

Latoya bought 80 markers.

4 tens + 3 tens = _____   5 tens + 1 ten= _____   2 tens + 7 tens = _____

60 + 30 = _____   40 + 20 = _____   80 + 10 = _____

50 + 30 = _____   10 + 40 = _____   70 + 10 = _____

$$
\begin{array}{r} 50 \\ +\,30 \\ \hline \end{array}
\qquad
\begin{array}{r} 40 \\ +\,40 \\ \hline \end{array}
\qquad
\begin{array}{r} 30 \\ +\,60 \\ \hline \end{array}
\qquad
\begin{array}{r} 20 \\ +\,50 \\ \hline \end{array}
$$

$$
\begin{array}{r} 70 \\ +\,40 \\ \hline \end{array}
\qquad
\begin{array}{r} 80 \\ +\,90 \\ \hline \end{array}
\qquad
\begin{array}{r} 40 \\ +\,90 \\ \hline \end{array}
\qquad
\begin{array}{r} 50 \\ +\,60 \\ \hline \end{array}
$$

Luis was playing basketball. He made 36 baskets and missed 20. How many times did Luis shoot for a basket?

$$36 = 30 + 6$$
$$+\,20 = 20 + 0$$
$$50 + 6 = 56$$

Step 1: Add the ones: 6 + 0 = 6.
Step 2: Add the tens: 3 + 2 = 5.

Luis shot for a basket 56 times.

54 + 30	72 + 10	80 + 46
39 + 40	60 + 64	81 + 40
96 + 80	58 + 60	83 +70
70 + 55	57 + 90	44 + 60

example

Two classes went on a museum trip together. There were 28 students in one class and 31 students in the other class. How many students went on this museum trip?

$$28 = 20 + 8$$
$$+ 31 = 30 + 1$$
$$50 + 9 = 59$$

Add the ones. Then add the tens.

There were 59 students on the museum trip.

64 + 33	32 + 45	27 + 51
81 + 14	56 + 40	17 + 32
35 + 33	55 + 24	31 + 15
53 + 24	27 + 21	15 + 33

examples

Kareem read 43 pages in his book. Later, he read 9 more pages. How many pages did Kareem read?

$$43 = 40 + 3$$
$$+9 = 0 + 9$$
$$\overline{40 + 12 = 52}$$

or

$$\overset{1}{4}3$$
$$+\,9$$
$$\overline{52}$$

Step 1: Add the ones: 3 + 9 = 12.
Step 2: Rename 10 ones as 1 ten:
*   12 ones = 1 ten and 2 ones.*
Step 3: Add the tens: 1 + 4 = 5.

Kareem read 52 pages.

64 + 18	87 + 8	39 + 55
43 + 8	56 + 27	17 + 58
63 + 19	50 + 48	76 + 18

example

> means "greater than."
< means "less than."
= means "equal."

83 + 7 _____<_____ 7 + 84

6 + 32 _____>_____ 6 + (30 + 1)

56 + 0 _____=_____ 50 + 6

Fill in the blanks with the correct symbol: >,<, or =. Look for secrets.

29 + 42 _____ 42 + 30

15 + 20 + 3 _____ 23 + 14

7 + 3 + 6 _____ 10 + 5

(7 + 3) + (6 + 4) + (9 + 1) + 4 _____ 10 + 10 + 10 + 6

85 + 96 _____ 96 + 85

79 + 0 _____ 77

My secrets are _____

_____

_____

example

Molly sold 224 tickets to the ice skating show. Bill sold 194 tickets. How many tickets did they sell?

$$\begin{array}{r}^{1}\\224\\+\ 194\\\hline 418\end{array}$$

Step 1: Add the ones: 4 + 4 = 8.

Step 2: Add the tens: 2 + 9 = 11. Rename 10 tens for 1 hundred: 11 tens = 1 hundred and 1 ten.

Step 3: Add the hundreds: 1 + 2 + 1 = 4.

They sold 418 tickets.

287 + 392	562 + 908	490 + 969	301 + 869
856 + 981	659 + 719	718 + 177	572 + 396
882 + 209	543 + 173	777 + 109	806 + 962

ADDITION

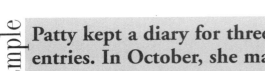

Patty kept a diary for three months. In September, she made 30 entries. In October, she made 31 entries. In November, she made 30 entries. How many entries did she make in all?

$$30 + 31 + 30 = 91 \qquad \textbf{or} \qquad \begin{array}{r} 30 \\ 31 \\ + 30 \\ \hline 91 \end{array}$$

Patty made 91 entries in her diary.

Tom bought 3 boxes of dog biscuits. The first box had 56 biscuits, the second 65 biscuits, and the third 48 biscuits. How many dog biscuits did Tom buy?

Equation: _____

Philip worked as a volunteer at an animal shelter for 5 hours on Sunday, 4 hours on Monday, 6 hours on Tuesday, and 3 hours on Wednesday. How many hours did Philip work at the shelter?

Equation: _____

Carmen went on a three-day car trip with her dad. They drove 256 miles the first day, 303 miles the second day, and 198 miles the third day. What was the total number of miles that they drove?

Equation: _____

Walter bought a TV for $350, a VCR for $149, and a remote control for $36. How much did he spend?

Equation: _____

Subtraction

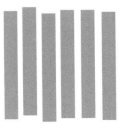

example

Phyllis had 12 counters and gave 3 to Danny. How many counters did Phyllis have left?

12 – 3 = ?

12 – 3 = 9
Phyllis had 9 counters left.

Write a subtraction equation for the picture.

_____

_____

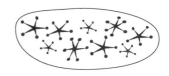

_____

Draw x's to find the difference.

11 – 7 = _____   15 – 9 = _____

13 – 3 = _____   7 – 7 = _____

6 – 0 = _____   9 – _____ = 5

43

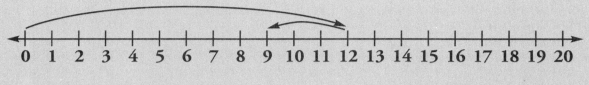

Nina biked 12 blocks, then came back 3 blocks. How far was Nina from where she started?

$12 - 3 = 9$

Nina was 9 blocks from where she started.

Write the subtraction equation for the number line.

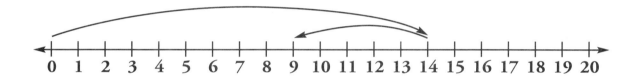

_____

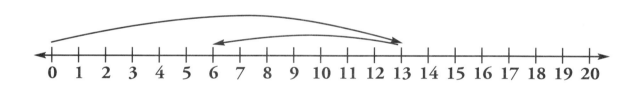

_____

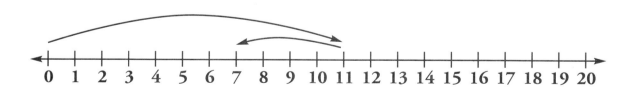

_____

Draw arrows on the number line to find the difference.

15 – 7 = _____

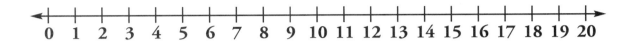

10 – 4 = _____

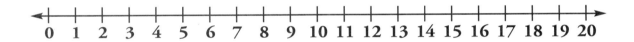

16 – 9 = _____

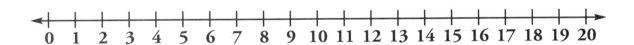

Write a story problem that uses subtraction. Then write the equation.

_____

_____

_____

example

How can you use the Addition Table on page 47 to subtract 11 – 6?

11 – 6 = ? means 6 + ? = 11

6 + 5 = 11

11 – 6 = 5

Complete the Addition Table. Then use the Addition Table to solve these equations.

16 – 9 = _____   13 – 4 = _____   10 – 6 = _____

11 – 3 = _____   7 – 3 = _____   7 + _____ = 15

18 – _____ = 9   9 – _____ = 4   11 – 7 = _____

_____ + 9 = 15   8 + _____ = 14   17 – _____ = 8

16 – 8 = _____   12 – 5 = _____   15 – 8 = _____

Write a subtraction story problem. Use the Addition Table to solve the problem.

_____

_____

_____

Addition Table

+	0	1	2	3	4	5	6	7	8	9
0										
1										
2										
3										
4										
5										
6						11				
7										
8										
9										

You are looking for secrets.
Find the difference.

8 – 1 = _____   12 – 1 = _____   7 – 1 = _____

What is your secret for subtracting 1 from a number?

_____

Find the difference.

9 – 0 = _____   12 – 0 = _____   4 – 0 = _____

What is your secret for subtracting 0 from a number?

_____

_____

example
How can you use addition to subtract 13 – 6 ?
13 – 6 = ? is the same as 6 + ? = 13.
6 + 7 = 13
13 – 6 = 7

Rename as addition to solve.

8 – 3 = _____   12 – 7 = _____

_____   _____

14 – 9 = _____   11 – 9 = _____

_____   _____

Strategies for Subtraction Facts

$10 - 7 =$ _____

_____

$9 - 6 =$ _____

_____

$15 - 7 =$ _____

_____

$12 - 4 =$ _____

_____

$13 - 5 =$ _____

_____

$16 - 9 =$ _____

_____

Solve. Use your secrets.

$12 - 6 =$ _____ $14 - 7 =$ _____ $16 - 8 =$ _____ $18 - 9 =$ _____

$10 - 6 =$ _____ $10 - 3 =$ _____ $10 - 8 =$ _____ $10 - 2 =$ _____

$11 - 4 =$ _____ $14 - 6 =$ _____ $8 - 5 =$ _____ $7 - 3 =$ _____

$13 - 9 =$ _____ $12 - 3 =$ _____ $15 - 8 =$ _____ $17 - 9 =$ _____

$13 - 1 =$ _____ $12 - 0 =$ _____ $9 - 9 =$ _____ $7 - 6 =$ _____

What other subtraction secrets did you use?

_____

_____

SUBTRACTION

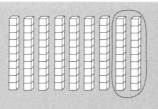

examples

90 – 20 = ?

9 tens – 2 tens = 7 tens

90 – 20 = 70

130 – 50 = ?

13 tens – 5 tens = 8 tens

130 – 50 = 80

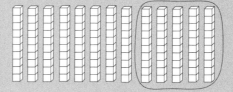

140 – 70 = _____   140 – 80 = _____

150 – 70 = _____   90 – 30 = _____

80 – 10 = _____   110 – 80 = _____

80 – 50 = _____   60 – 60 = _____

120 – 60 = _____   130 – 40 = _____

130 – 90 = _____   140 – 70 = _____

110 – 90 = _____   110 – 40 = _____

My secret for subtracting multiples of 10 is _____

_____

_____

example

73 students want to go to the after–school program. 39 students said they cannot go on Tuesdays. About how many students can go on Tuesdays?

Round 73 and 39 to the nearest 10.
$73 \rightarrow 70$
$39 \rightarrow 40$

$70 - 40 = 30$
About 30 students can go on Tuesdays.

Round to the nearest 10 to estimate.

92 – 57

_____ – _____ = _____

75 – 18

_____ – _____ = _____

66 – 49

_____ – _____ = _____

83 – 28

_____ – _____ = _____

45 – 19

_____ – _____ = _____

54 – 36

_____ – _____ = _____

88 – 24

_____ – _____ = _____

63 – 15

_____ – _____ = _____

51

SUBTRACTION

example

Amos had $8.79. He bought a snack for $2.43. About how many dollars did he have left?

Round $8.79 and $2.43 to the nearest dollar.

$8.79 → $9

$2.43 → $2

$9 − $2 = $7

Amos had about $7 left.

Round to the nearest dollar to estimate.

$6.78 − $4.01

$ _____ − $ _____ = $ _____

$9.21 − $3.15

$ _____ − $ _____ = $ _____

$8.63 − $7.58

$ _____ − $ _____ = $ _____

$5.74 − $2.51

$ _____ − $ _____ = $ _____

$9.21 − $4.44

$ _____ − $ _____ = $ _____

$6.77 − $1.80

$ _____ − $ _____ = $ _____

$5.18 − $1.98

$ _____ − $ _____ = $ _____

$3.48 − $2.39

$ _____ − $ _____ = $ _____

example

Clarence is taping a movie that is 89 minutes long. He has already taped 24 minutes of the movie. How many minutes does Clarence have left to tape?

89 – 24 = ?

$$89 = 80 + 9$$
$$\underline{-\ 24 = 20 + 4}$$
$$65 = 60 + 5$$

Step 1: Subtract the ones: 9 – 4 = 5.

Step 2: Subtract the tens: 8 tens – 2 tens = 6 tens.

Clarence has 65 minutes left to tape.

78 – 36	54 – 14	48 – 26
95 – 34	85 – 72	93 – 51
67 – 13	86 – 55	87 – 45

Create a story problem that uses subtraction with no renaming.

_____

_____

_____

SUBTRACTION

example

Regina's team played 32 soccer games. Her team lost or tied 14 games. How many games did Regina's team win?

$32 = 30 + 2 = \mathbf{20 + 12}$ *Step 1: You need more ones. Rename 32 to*
$\underline{-14} = 10 + 4 = \underline{\mathbf{10 + \ \ 4}}$ *2 tens and 12 ones.*
$\qquad\qquad\qquad\quad 10 + \ \ 8$ *Step 2: Subtract the ones: 12 − 4 = 8.*
$\qquad\qquad\qquad\qquad 18$ *Step 3: Subtract the tens: 2 tens − 1 ten = 1 ten*

Regina's team won 18 games.

example

$695 = 600 + 90 + 5 = \mathbf{600 + 80 + 15}$
$\underline{-258} = 200 + 50 + 8 = \underline{\mathbf{200 + 50 + \ \ 8}}$
$\qquad\qquad\qquad\qquad\quad \mathbf{400 + 30 + \ \ 7}$
$\qquad\qquad\qquad\qquad\qquad 437$

$$\begin{array}{r} 68 \\ -29 \\ \hline \end{array} \qquad \begin{array}{r} 47 \\ -18 \\ \hline \end{array} \qquad \begin{array}{r} 92 \\ -37 \\ \hline \end{array}$$

$$\begin{array}{r} 65 \\ -28 \\ \hline \end{array} \qquad \begin{array}{r} 693 \\ -248 \\ \hline \end{array} \qquad \begin{array}{r} 530 \\ -314 \\ \hline \end{array}$$

$$\begin{array}{r} 851 \\ -147 \\ \hline \end{array} \qquad \begin{array}{r} 764 \\ -338 \\ \hline \end{array} \qquad \begin{array}{r} 85 \\ -27 \\ \hline \end{array}$$

example

John is the editor of a newspaper that is delivered to 854 people. 483 papers are delivered to men. How many papers are delivered to women?

$$854 = 800 + 50 + 4 = 700 + 150 + 4$$
$$\underline{-\ 483 = 400 + 80 + 3 = \underline{400 + 80 + 3}}$$
$$300 + 70 + 1$$
$$371$$

Step 1: Subtract the ones: 4 – 3 = 1.

Step 2: You need more tens. Rename 854 to 7 hundreds, 15 tens, and 4 ones.

Step 3: Subtract the tens: 15 tens – 8 tens = 7 tens.

Step 4: Subtract the hundreds: 7 hundreds – 4 hundreds = 3 hundreds.

The paper is delivered to 371 women.

753	842	435
− 382	− 591	− 193

615	573	658
− 474	− 283	− 273

744	953	620
− 480	− 762	− 350

example

Tammy checked her subtraction problem with addition.

$$
\begin{array}{r} 98 \\ -35 \\ \hline 63 \end{array} \qquad \begin{array}{r} 63 \\ +35 \\ \hline 98 \end{array}
$$

Step 1: *Add the difference to the number subtracted.*

Step 2: *The sum should be the original number.*

Use addition to check the difference. Circle any incorrect answers.

$$
\begin{array}{r} 53 \\ -12 \\ \hline 39 \end{array} \qquad\qquad \begin{array}{r} 72 \\ -48 \\ \hline 24 \end{array} \qquad\qquad \begin{array}{r} 853 \\ -537 \\ \hline 326 \end{array}
$$

$$
\begin{array}{r} 765 \\ -328 \\ \hline 438 \end{array} \qquad\qquad \begin{array}{r} 73 \\ -37 \\ \hline 46 \end{array} \qquad\qquad \begin{array}{r} 816 \\ -254 \\ \hline 662 \end{array}
$$

Find the difference. Then check the answer using addition.

$$
\begin{array}{r} 78 \\ -49 \\ \hline \end{array} \qquad\qquad \begin{array}{r} 564 \\ -343 \\ \hline \end{array} \qquad\qquad \begin{array}{r} 873 \\ -491 \\ \hline \end{array}
$$

$$
\begin{array}{r} 970 \\ -628 \\ \hline \end{array} \qquad\qquad \begin{array}{r} 38 \\ -19 \\ \hline \end{array} \qquad\qquad \begin{array}{r} 62 \\ -27 \\ \hline \end{array}
$$

Tala wants to swim 60 laps in the pool. She has 43 more laps to go. How many laps did Tala swim?

$$\begin{array}{r} 60 \\ -\ 43 \\ \hline 17 \end{array}$$

Tala swam 17 laps.

Bryan has to read 156 pages. He has read 119 pages. How many pages does he have left to read?

Equation: _____

Ruby received 8 stuffed animals for her birthday. Now she has a total of 36 stuffed animals. How many stuffed animals did she have before her birthday?

Equation: _____

Emily weighs 72 pounds. She has gained 18 pounds since her last checkup. How much did Emily weigh then?

Equation: _____

The odometer on Manuel's new sports car has 564 miles on it. This morning it read 483 miles. How far did Manuel drive his car today?

Equation: _____

John is on a bike trip. The entire distance is 86 miles. He has just reached the 59–mile marker. How many miles does John have left to bike?

Equation: _____

Write and solve a story problem that uses subtraction with renaming.

_____

_____

_____

Solve the 2–step problem.

Sara helped with the horses in the stable. She worked 15 hours the first week and 18 hours the second week. After the third week, she had worked a total of 49 hours. How many hours did Sara work during the third week?

Equation: _____

Make up and solve a 2–step story problem.

_____

_____

Multiplication

example

Martin's file cabinets are arranged in an array. What is the name of the array?

There are 4 rows with 3 drawers in each row.

The name of the array is 4 x 3.
The factors are 4 and 3.

Write the name of the array and give the factors.

```
X X X X X
X X X X X
X X X X X
X X X X X
X X X X X
X X X X X
```

```
X X X X X X X
X X X X X X X
X X X X X X X
```

```
X X X
X X X
X X X
X X X
X X X
X X X
X X X
```

_____

_____

_____

_____

_____

_____

```
X  X  X  X
X  X  X  X
X  X  X  X
X  X  X  X
```

```
X X X X X X
X X X X X X
X X X X X X
X X X X X X
X X X X X X
X X X X X X
X X X X X X
```

```
X
X
```

_____

_____

_____

_____

example

Tunesia arranged her books in a 5 by 2 array.
What equation tells how many books she has?

An array is a way of showing multiplication:
$5 \times 2 = 10$.

Tunesia has 10 books.

Use X's.

an array with the factors 6 and 3

a 5 by 4 array

an array for the equation 8 x 3 = 24

 an array with a factor of 3 and the product 21

 all possible arrays for the product 12

example

Sal has 5 toy wagons. Each wagon is 6 inches long. He put the wagons on a track. How many inches of track do the wagons cover?

$6 + 6 + 6 + 6 + 6 = 30$ or $5 \times 6 = 30$

The wagons cover 30 inches of track.

Solve. Then write as a multiplication equation.

$7 + 7 + 7 + 7 =$ _____

_____

$9 + 9 + 9 =$ _____

_____

$1 + 1 + 1 + 1 + 1 + 1 + 1 + 1 + 1 =$ _____

$5 + 5 + 5 + 5 + 5 + 5 =$ _____

_____

$4 + 4 + 4 + 4 + 4 + 4 + 4 + 4 =$ _____

_____

$6 + 6 + 6 + 6 + 6 + 6 + 6 + 6 =$ _____

_____

Write an addition equation and multiplication equation.

XXX   XXX   XXX   XXX   XXX   XXX   XXX   XXX   XXX

_____   _____

MULTIPLICATION

Pam wants to fill 7 bags with chocolates for her party. She will put 3 chocolates in each bag. How many chocolates does Pam need?

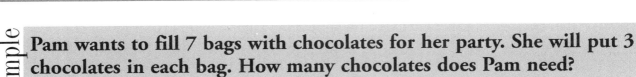

There are 7 groups of 3.

$7 \times 3 = 21$

Pam needs 21 chocolates.

Use X's to draw the groups. Write the multiplication equation.

4 groups of 7   1 group of 2

_____   _____

2 groups of 9   9 groups of 3

_____   _____

5 groups of 1   3 groups of 4

_____   _____

Dennis stopped his bike every 3 blocks. He stopped 6 times. How many blocks did he ride?

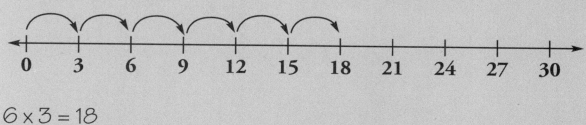

$6 \times 3 = 18$
Dennis rode 18 blocks.

Look at the number line. Write a multiplication equation for what it shows.

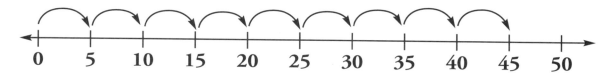

_____

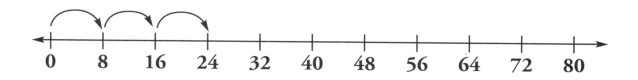

_____

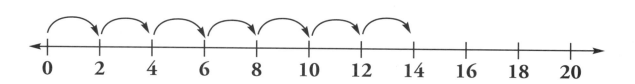

_____

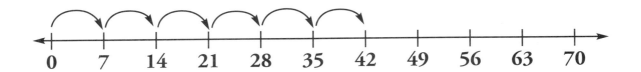

_____

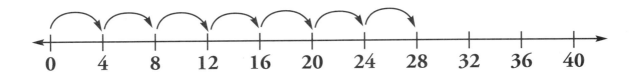

_____

Show 7 x 9 on the number line. Write the equation.

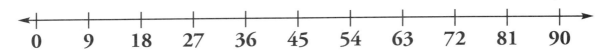

_____

Show 8 x 6 on the number line. Write the equation.

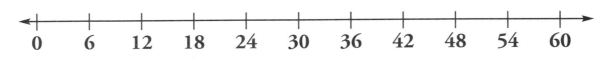

_____

example

Which has more stamps?

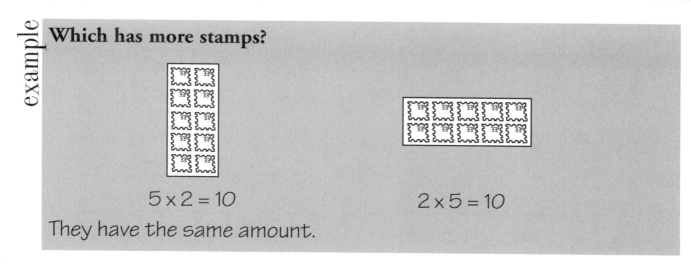

$5 \times 2 = 10$

$2 \times 5 = 10$

They have the same amount.

Write the multiplication equation for each exercise.

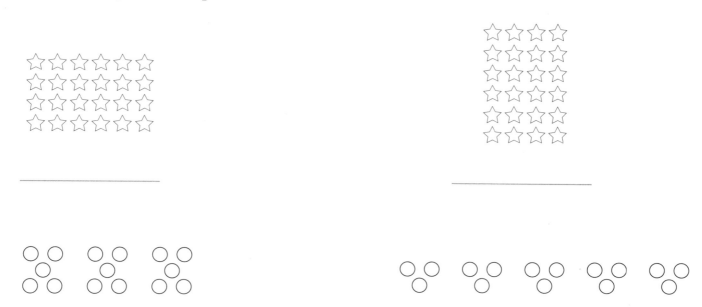

_____

_____

_____

_____

MULTIPLICATION

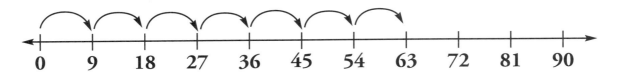

_____

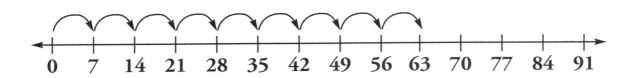

_____

5 + 5 + 5 + 5 + 5 + 5 + 5 = _____   7 + 7 + 7 + 7 + 7 = _____

_____   _____

What did you notice about each pair of exercises? _____

_____

My secret is _____

_____

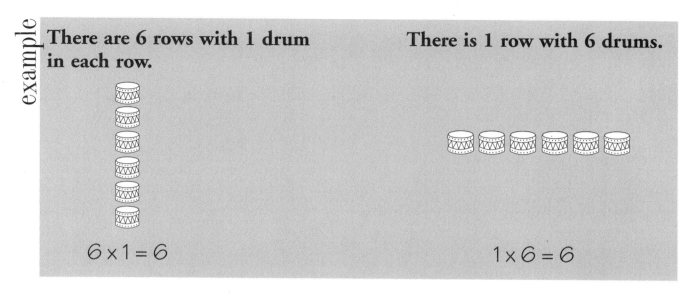

example

There are **6 rows** with **1 drum** in each row.

$6 \times 1 = 6$

There is **1 row** with **6 drums.**

$1 \times 6 = 6$

Write a multiplication equation for each array. Look for the secret.

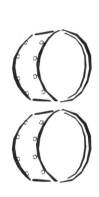

_____   _____   _____

_____   _____

$7 \times 1 =$ _____ $29 \times 1 =$ _____ $276 \times 1 =$ _____

$1 \times 985 =$ _____ $1 \times 490 =$ _____ $1 \times 555 =$ _____

_____ $\times 76 = 76$ $543 \times$ _____ $= 543$ $1 \times$ _____ $= 632$

My secret for multiplying by one is _____

_____

 $n \times 1 =$ _____ $1 \times 1{,}000{,}000 =$ _____

 $17 \times 1 \times 1 \times 1 \times 1 \times 1 \times 1 \times 1 \times 1 \times 1 \times 1 =$ _____

$6 \times (5 - 4) \times (17 - 16) \times (100 - 99) =$ _____

example

JuJu searched her pockets for coins. She looked in 8 pockets. In each pocket, she found 0 coins. How many coins did she find?

$8 \times 0 = 0$

JuJu found 0 coins.

Look for the secret.

9 x 0 = _____   0 x 15 = _____   476 x 0 = _____

0 x 854 = _____   0 x 920 = _____   651 x 0 = _____

_____ x 58 = 0   91 x _____ = 0   1 x _____ = 0

My secret for multiplying by zero is _____

_____

 n x 0 = _____   0 x 1,000,000 = _____

 18 x 63 x 0 x 19 x 476 x 99 = _____

 7 x (9 − 9) x 67 x 54 x 870 x 123 x 754 = _____

MULTIPLICATION

example **The Multiplication Table on page 73 shows that 2 x 3 = 6. Explain.**
The factors 2 and 3 are on the side and top of the table. They meet at the product 6.

Fill in the rest of the products on the table.
Look for patterns and secrets.

What patterns and secrets did you find on the multiplication table? _____

_____

_____

_____

Multiplication Table

x	1	2	3	4	5	6	7	8	9	10
1										
2			6							
3										
4										
5										
6										
7										
8										
9										
10										

MULTIPLICATION

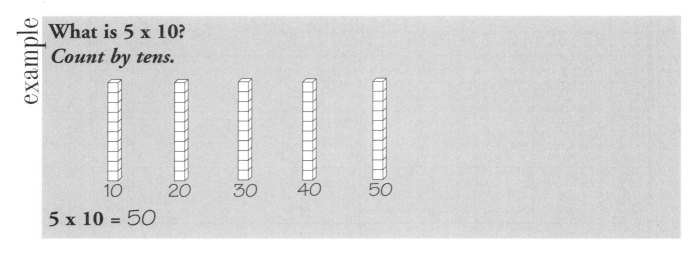

What is 5 x 10?
Count by tens.

10   20   30   40   50

5 x 10 = 50

Show 9 x 10 on a number line. Write the product.

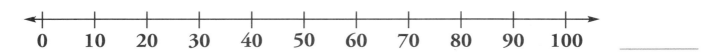

0   10   20   30   40   50   60   70   80   90   100   _____

Find the product.

8 x 10 = _____   4 x 10 = _____   7 x 10 = _____   12 x 10 = _____

Look for a secret. Then complete the table.

5	50
6	
9	
15	
3	
	90
	200
	1200

My secret for multiplying by 10 is _____

_____

_____

_____

example

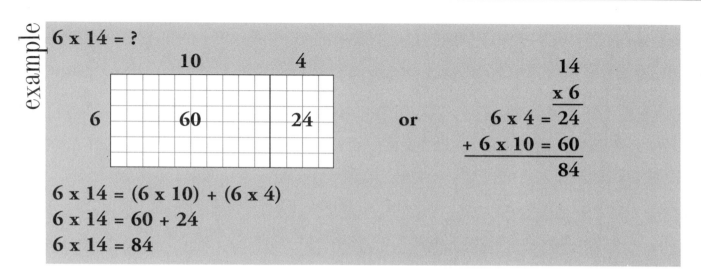

6 x 14 = ?

6 x 14 = (6 x 10) + (6 x 4)

6 x 14 = 60 + 24

6 x 14 = 84

Write the partial products inside the rectangle. Add to find the product.

9 x 12 = _____

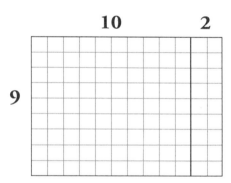

_____ + _____ = _____

7 x 16 = _____

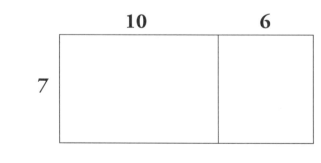

_____ + _____ = _____

5 x 13 = _____

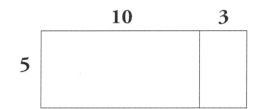

_____ + _____ = _____

4 x 18 = _____

```
       10            8
  ┌───────────┬───────────┐
4 │           │           │
  └───────────┴───────────┘
```

_____ + _____ = _____

 Fill in the blanks.

6 x 16 = (6 x _____) + (6 x _____)

6 x 16 = _____ + _____

6 x 16 = _____

example

In the auditorium, there are 7 rows with 28 seats in each row. How many seats are there in all?

7 x 28 = ?

	20	**8**
7	**140**	**56**

$$\begin{array}{r} 28 \\ \times\ 7 \\ \hline 56 \\ +\ 140 \\ \hline 196 \end{array}$$

There are 196 seats in all.

Use any method to find the product.

$$\begin{array}{r} 16 \\ \times\ 3 \\ \hline \end{array}$$
$$\begin{array}{r} 54 \\ \times\ 7 \\ \hline \end{array}$$
$$\begin{array}{r} 37 \\ \times\ 9 \\ \hline \end{array}$$

17 x 9 = _____   27 x 3 = _____   68 x 5 = _____

example

Look for the secret. What was done to *A* to get to *B* ? What is the equation?

A	B
9	45
6	30
4	20
1	5
0	0
8	40
10	50

***A* was multiplied by 5.**

$A \times 5 = B$

Can you find the secret? Complete the chart. Then write the equations.

A	B
4	12
7	21
3	
5	
11	
12	
	18

A	B
4	16
6	
3	12
	0
	4
10	
	32

A	B
5	45
6	
2	18
3	
1	
13	
0	

example

We use charts to show information.

Number of Weeks (W)	Number of Days (D)
1	7
2	14
3	21
4	28
5	35

The number of weeks times 7 equals the number of days.

$W \times 7 = D$

Complete the chart.
Write the equation.

Number of Cars (C)	Number of Wheels (W)
1	4
2	
3	
4	
5	
6	

Number of Triangles (T)	Number of Sides (S)
1	3
2	
3	
4	
5	
6	

_____   _____

Number of Chickens (C)	Number of Legs (L)
1	2
2	
3	
4	
5	
6	

Number of Dogs (D)	Number of Biscuits (B)
1	1
2	2
3	
4	
5	
6	

_____

Make a chart for the equations.

_____ x 6 = _____

_____ x 5 = _____

80

example

Why is 9 a square number?

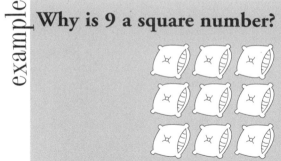

9 is the product of 3 x 3. A 3 by 3 array forms a square.

Use X's to draw an array.
Write the square number.

5 x 5 = _____   6 x 6 = _____

2 x 2 = _____   4 x 4 = _____

1 x 1 = _____   7 x 7 = _____

List 3 more square numbers.

MULTIPLICATION

example

> means "greater than."

< means "less than."

= means "equal."

Fill in the blank. Use >, <, or =.

5 x 5 ___>___ 7 x 0

7 x 3 ___<___ 7 x 6

6 x 4 ___=___ 8 x 3

Write >, <, or =.

6 x 2 _____ 6 x 3

6 x 8 _____ 8 x 6

19 x 2 _____ (10 x 2) + (9 x 2)

4 x 5 _____ 5 x 5

1 x 8 _____ 6 x 1

9 x 6 x 0 x 7 _____ 3 x 2

5 x 4 _____ 4 + 4 + 4 + 4 + 4

Cloe bought 6 ski lessons. Each lesson cost $24. What was the total cost for Cloe's ski lessons?

Equation: _____

The ski trail was 7 miles long. Jamal liked it so much that he skied the same trail 13 times. How many miles did Jamal ski on that trail?

Equation: _____

The chair lift took 16 minutes to reach the top. Louis took the lift 4 times. How many minutes did he spend on the chair lift?

Equation: _____

Molly skied on 18 different trails this winter. She skied on each trail 3 times. How many ski runs did she make?

Equation: _____

The cafeteria has 24 tables. Each table can seat 8 people. How many people can sit in the cafeteria?

Equation: _____

Yancy bought 6 containers of orange juice for his family and friends. Each orange juice cost $.65 (65 cents). How much money did Yancy spend on orange juice?

Equation: _____

Arturo bought 6 energy bars. Each bar cost $.45 (45 cents). How much did Arturo spend on energy bars?

Equation: _____

What was the total cost of the orange juice and energy bars that Yancy and Arturo bought?

Equation: _____

Division: Part One

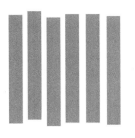

example

Clementine pasted 8 photos of horses on a chart. She arranged the photos in an array with 4 rows.
How many photos did she put in each row?

Clementine put 2 photos in each row.

Draw an array to solve the problem.

Katie pasted 18 horse photos in her album. She put 2 photos in each row. How many rows of horse photos are in her album? _____

Tyler is putting 24 photos of his birthday party into his photo album. He wants to put them in 6 rows. How many photos will he put in each row? _____

Dana's album has 21 photos from a family vacation. There are 3 photos in each row. How many rows are there? _____

Darrell has 20 photos of his soccer game. He pasted them in 4 rows. How many photos are in each row? _____

My secret is _____

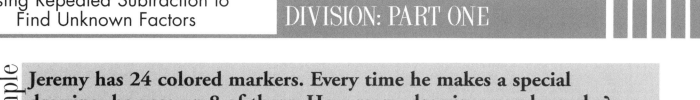

example

Jeremy has 24 colored markers. Every time he makes a special drawing, he uses up 8 of them. How many drawings can he make?

$$
\begin{array}{r}
24 \\
-\ 8 \\
\hline
16 \\
-\ 8 \\
\hline
8 \\
-\ 8 \\
\hline
0
\end{array}
$$

Step 1: Begin with 24.

Step 2: Keep subtracting 8 until the answer is 0.

Step 3: Count the number of times 8 was subtracted.

8 was subtracted 3 times.

There are three 8's in 24.

Jeremy can make 3 drawings.

Use repeated subtraction.

How many 7's are in 35? _____   How many 6's are in 42? _____

How many 9's are in 45? _____   How many 8's are in 56? _____

How many 12's are in 108? _____   How many 4's are in 52? _____

My secret is _____

_____

_____

example

Belinda made a train track with rods that equal 15. How many tracks of 3 did she need?

She needed 5 tracks of 3.

Use rods to solve.

How many 4's are in 28? _____   How many 8s' are in 32? _____

How many of 9's are in 72? _____   How many 7's are in 49? _____

How many 3's are in 27? _____   How many 5's are in 25? _____

How many 2's are in 18? _____   How many 6's are in 24? _____

My secret is _____

_____

_____

example

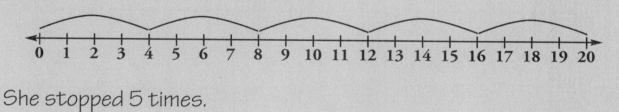

Brianne walked 20 blocks to school. She stopped every 4 blocks to adjust her backpack. How many times did she stop?

She stopped 5 times.

Use the number line. Circle the stops.

Walk 21 blocks and stop every 7 blocks.

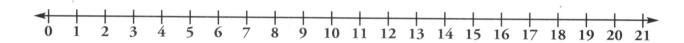

Stops: _____

Walk 16 blocks and stop every 2 blocks.

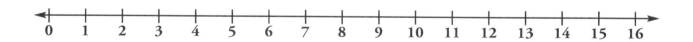

Stops: _____

Walk 24 blocks and stop every 6 blocks.

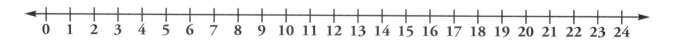

Stops: _____

Walk 56 blocks and stop every 8 blocks.

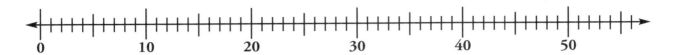

Stops: _____

Walk 42 blocks and stop every 7 blocks.

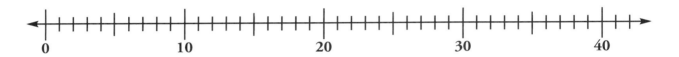

Stops: _____

What is your secret for figuring out the number of stops?

_____

_____

_____

_____

example

Jerome used 24 cubes to make trains. He put 4 cubes in each train. How many trains did Jerome make?

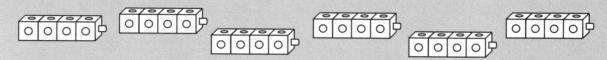

There are 6 groups of 4 in 24.

Jerome made 6 trains.

Draw X's to solve each problem.

12 cubes
3 in each train

_____ trains

27 cubes
3 in each train

_____ trains

35 cubes
5 in each train

_____ trains

54 cubes
9 in each train

_____ trains

30 cubes
5 in each train

_____ trains

32 cubes
4 in each train

_____ trains

example

The remote control has 18 buttons in 6 rows. How many buttons are in each row?

6 x 3 = 18
18 ÷ 6 = 3

There are 3 buttons in each row.

Solve. Then write a division equation.

8 x _____ = 32

_____

7 x _____ = 21

_____

5 x _____ = 45

_____

_____ x 6 = 42

_____

_____ x 8 = 40

_____

_____ x 9 = 27

_____

4 x _____ =16

_____

8 x _____ = 56

_____

_____ x 7 = 49

_____

8 x _____ = 8

_____

example

Write 4 equations for this array using multiplication and division.

$4 \times 7 = 28$

$7 \times 4 = 28$

$28 \div 7 = 4$

$28 \div 4 = 7$

Write 4 equations for each array.

_____

_____

_____

_____

_____

_____

_____

_____

_____

_____

_____

_____

Write 4 equations for each group of numbers.

24, 3, 8   6, 9, 54   5, 20, 4

_____

_____

_____

_____

_____

_____

_____

_____

_____

_____

_____

_____

example

Write the division equation that undoes the multiplication equation.

Ben put 2 marbles at a time into a bowl. He did this 6 times. There were 12 marbles in the bowl. Ben then took 2 marbles at a time out of the bowl until it was empty. How many times did he take marbles out of the bowl?

6 x 2 = 12

12 ÷ 2 = 6

Ben took marbles out of the bowl 6 times.

Write an equation to undo each of the following equations.

9 x 3 = 27   6 x 9 = 54   8 x 7 = 56

_____   _____   _____

4 x 8 = 32   7 x 7 = 49   3 x 5 = 15

_____   _____   _____

24 ÷ 8 = 3   28 ÷ 7 = 4   42 ÷ 7 = 6

_____   _____   _____

Solve.

25 ÷ 5 = _____   64 ÷ 8 = _____   63 ÷ 9 = _____

What division equation is shown on the Multiplication Table?

Since $6 \times 7 = 42$, $42 \div 7 = 6$

Fill in each gray box.

Multiplication Table

x	0	1	2	3	4	5	6	7	8
0									
1									
2									
3									
4									
5									
6								42	
7									
8									

Write a multiplication equation and division equation for each gray box on page 97.

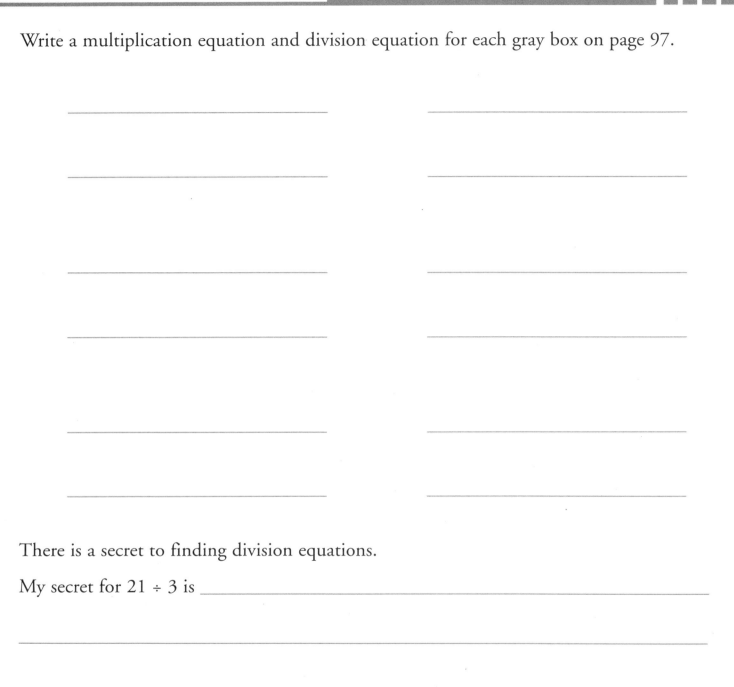

There is a secret to finding division equations.

My secret for 21 ÷ 3 is _____

_____

_____

example

Sarah had 12 marbles. She put the same number in each of 3 bags.
How many marbles are in each bag?

12 ÷ 3 = ?

12 ÷ 3 = 4
There are 4 marbles in each bag.

18 ÷ 2 = _____   24 ÷ 6 = _____

27 ÷ 3 = _____   35 ÷ 5 = _____

28 ÷ 4 = _____   36 ÷ 6 = _____

9 ÷ 9 = _____   7 ÷ 1 = _____

0 ÷ 5 = _____   32 ÷ 8 = _____

example

Janet practiced the piano for 40 minutes. She played the same piece 8 times. How many minutes did it take her to play the piece once?

$40 \div 8 = 5$

It took Janet 5 minutes to play the piece once.

Kona saw 24 monkeys at the zoo. The same number of monkeys were in each of 3 cages. How many monkeys were in each cage?

Equation: _____

Arlene swam 9 laps in the pool. She swam at an even pace for 18 minutes. How long did it take her to swim one lap?

Equation: _____

Clay baked 3 dozen cookies (1 dozen = 12). He put the same number of cookies on each of 4 cookie trays. How many cookies were on each tray?

Equation: _____

Cora jogged around the pond for 30 minutes. It took her 3 minutes each time. How many times did she jog around the pond?

Equation: _____

40 people entered a skateboarding competition. The same number of people signed up for each of 5 events. How many people signed up for each event?

Equation: _____

Ed put 36 boxes on 4 shelves. He placed the same number of boxes on each shelf. How many boxes did Ed put on each shelf?

Equation: _____

example

Ping had 6 stuffed animals. She put them all into 1 box. How many stuffed animals are in the box?

$6 \div 1 = 6$
There are 6 stuffed animals in the box.

15 ÷ 1 = _____   24 ÷ 1 = _____

38 ÷ 1= _____   73 ÷ 1= _____

My secret for dividing a number by 1 is _____

_____

example

Pat has 6 stuffed animals. She put the same number into 6 boxes. How many stuffed animals are in each box?

$6 \div 6 = 1$
There is one stuffed animal in each box.

16 ÷ 16 = _____   23 ÷ 23 = _____

19 ÷ 19 = _____   76 ÷ 76 = _____

My secret for dividing a number by itself is _____

_____

example

Look for the secret in the table.

X	Y
15	3
10	2
35	7
45	9
5	1
40	8

$X \div 5 = Y$

Find the secret and complete the table.

X	Y
16	8
4	2
10	
8	
6	
12	
2	
48	

X	Y
24	8
15	5
3	1
12	
9	
18	
30	
300	

Secret: _____

Secret: _____

X	Y
24	6
12	3
4	
32	
40	
20	
36	
800	

X	Y
36	6
12	2
24	
6	
54	
18	
60	
48	

Secret: _____

Secret: _____

Create your own tables. Write the secret of each table.

X	Y

X	Y

Secret: _____

Secret: _____

103

Addition and Subtraction

ADDITION AND SUBTRACTION

example

Charmaine was playing a game with Andy. Her scores were 86, 41, and 39. What was her total score?

86 + 41 + 39 = ?

$$
\begin{array}{r}
\overset{1}{8}6 \\
41 \\
+\ 39 \\
\hline
166
\end{array}
$$

Step 1: Add the ones: 6 + 1 + 9 = 16.
Step 2: Rename 10 ones to 1 ten: 16 ones = 1 ten and 6 ones
Step 3: Add the tens: 1 + 8 + 4 + 3 = 16

Charmaine's total score was 166 .

$$
\begin{array}{r}
48 \\
62 \\
+\ 55 \\
\hline
\end{array}
\qquad
\begin{array}{r}
22 \\
34 \\
+\ 16 \\
\hline
\end{array}
\qquad
\begin{array}{r}
87 \\
93 \\
24 \\
+\ 6 \\
\hline
\end{array}
$$

$$
\begin{array}{r}
94 \\
17 \\
33 \\
+\ 88 \\
\hline
\end{array}
\qquad
\begin{array}{r}
87 \\
22 \\
+\ 48 \\
\hline
\end{array}
\qquad
\begin{array}{r}
10 \\
98 \\
+\ 52 \\
\hline
\end{array}
$$

28 + 99 + 72 = _____   53 + 9 + 80 = _____   17 + 84 + 66 + 96 = _____

example

At the marathon, there were 2,986 runners and 3,984 spectators. How many people were at the marathon?

2,986 + 3,984 = ?

```
  1 1 1
  2,986        Add each place starting with the ones. Rename as necessary.
+ 3,984
  6,970
```

There were 6,970 people at the marathon.

984	388	9,087	7,692
+ 668	+ 254	1,832	+ 2,953
		+ 4,470	

536	872	2,565	6,742
621	+ 398	+ 7,894	+ 1,471
+ 295			

987 + 685 + 335 = _____   860 + 75 + 852 = _____   9,087 + 87 + 342 + 3,855 = _____

Favorite Flavors of Ice Cream	
Flavors	Votes
chocolate	32,853
vanilla	29,889
strawberry	19,320
cherry	15,932
fudge	15,425
mint	14,568

How many people chose chocolate, vanilla, or strawberry?

Equation: _____

How many people chose mint, cherry, or vanilla?

Equation: _____

How many people chose fudge or mint?

Equation: _____

 How many people voted?

Equation: _____

examples

Jasmine had $83. She spent $29. How much money did she have left?

$83 − $29 = ?

$$
\begin{array}{rcl}
\overset{7\ 13}{\$8\cancel{3}} & = & 70 + 13 \\
-\ \$29 & = & -\ 20 + 9 \\
\hline
\$54 & = & 50 + 4 \\
& = & \$54
\end{array}
$$

Step 1: There are not enough ones. Rename
1 ten to 10 ones.

Step 2: Subtract the ones: 13 − 9 = 4.

Step 3: Subtract the tens: 7 − 2 = 5.

Jasmine had $54 left.

Mr. Chavez had $563. He spent $293. How much money did he have left?

$$
\begin{array}{rcl}
\overset{4\ 16}{\$5\cancel{6}3} & = & 400 + 160 + 3 \\
-\ \$293 & = & -\ 200 + 90 + 3 \\
\hline
\$270 & = & 200 + 70 + 0 \\
& = & \$270
\end{array}
$$

Step 1: Subtract the ones: 3 − 3 = 0.

Step 2: There are not enough tens.
　　　　Rename 1 hundred to 10 tens.

Step 3: Subtract the tens: 16 − 9 = 7.

Step 4: Subtract the hundreds: 4− 2 =2.

Mr. Chavez had $270 left.

$$
\begin{array}{ccc}
\begin{array}{r} 95 \\ -\ 39 \\ \hline \end{array} &
\begin{array}{r} 61 \\ -\ 42 \\ \hline \end{array} &
\begin{array}{r} 73 \\ -\ 49 \\ \hline \end{array}
\end{array}
$$

$$
\begin{array}{ccc}
\begin{array}{r} 572 \\ -\ 281 \\ \hline \end{array} &
\begin{array}{r} 954 \\ -536 \\ \hline \end{array} &
\begin{array}{r} 756 \\ -\ 276 \\ \hline \end{array}
\end{array}
$$

76 − 18 = _____   287 − 96 = _____   388 − 291 = _____

example

There were 872 tickets sold for the movie. Children bought 296 of the tickets. How many ticket holders were not children?

$$
\begin{array}{r}
\overset{16}{\overset{7\ \cancel{\it 8}\ 12}{872}} \\
-\ 296 \\
\hline
576
\end{array}
\quad
\begin{array}{rcrcrcr}
 & = & 700 & + & 160 & + & 12 \\
 & = - & 200 & + & 90 & + & 6 \\
\hline
 & = & 500 & + & 70 & + & 6 \\
 & = & 576 & & & &
\end{array}
$$

Step 1: There are not enough ones or tens.
      Rename 1 ten to 10 ones AND
      rename 1 hundred to 10 tens.
Step 2: Subtract the ones: 12 – 6 = 6.
Step 3: Subtract the tens: 16 – 9 = 7.
Step 4: Subtract the hundreds: 7 – 2 = 5.

Children did not buy 576 of the tickets.

$$
\begin{array}{r}
976 \\
-\ 287 \\
\hline
\end{array}
\qquad\qquad
\begin{array}{r}
573 \\
-\ 185 \\
\hline
\end{array}
\qquad\qquad
\begin{array}{r}
254 \\
-\ 187 \\
\hline
\end{array}
$$

$$
\begin{array}{r}
731 \\
-\ 472 \\
\hline
\end{array}
\qquad\qquad
\begin{array}{r}
761 \\
-\ 588 \\
\hline
\end{array}
\qquad\qquad
\begin{array}{r}
635 \\
-\ 299 \\
\hline
\end{array}
$$

$$
\begin{array}{r}
371 \\
-\ 285 \\
\hline
\end{array}
\qquad\qquad
\begin{array}{r}
553 \\
-\ 276 \\
\hline
\end{array}
\qquad\qquad
\begin{array}{r}
958 \\
-\ 479 \\
\hline
\end{array}
$$

$356 - 198 =$ _____ $735 - 296 =$ _____ $844 - 256 =$ _____

ADDITION AND SUBTRACTION

example

The regular price of the ice skates is $208. The sale price is $24 less. What is the sale price?

1 10

$$\begin{array}{r} 2\cancel{0}8 \\ -\ 24 \\ \hline 184 \end{array}$$

Step 1: Subtract the ones: 8 − 4 = 4.
Step 2: There are not enough tens. Rename 1 hundred to 10 tens.
Step 3: Subtract the tens: 10 − 2 = 8.
Step 4: Subtract the hundreds: 1 − 0 = 1.

The sale price is $184.

$$\begin{array}{r} 70 \\ -\ 39 \\ \hline \end{array} \qquad \begin{array}{r} 706 \\ -\ 253 \\ \hline \end{array} \qquad \begin{array}{r} 804 \\ -\ 297 \\ \hline \end{array}$$

$$\begin{array}{r} 950 \\ -\ 263 \\ \hline \end{array} \qquad \begin{array}{r} 503 \\ -\ 274 \\ \hline \end{array} \qquad \begin{array}{r} 702 \\ -\ 365 \\ \hline \end{array}$$

$$\begin{array}{r} 180 \\ -\ 96 \\ \hline \end{array} \qquad \begin{array}{r} 505 \\ -\ 334 \\ \hline \end{array} \qquad \begin{array}{r} 990 \\ -\ 296 \\ \hline \end{array}$$

270 − 193 = _____   505 − 138 = _____   690 − 291 = _____

example

All 900 students in the school were invited on a trip to an ice skating rink. 135 students did not go. How many students did go?

$$
\begin{array}{rcl}
\overset{8\ \overset{9}{\cancel{10}}\ 10}{\cancel{900}} & = & 800 + 90 + 10 \\
-\ 135 & = & 100 + 30 + 5 \\
\hline
& = & 700 + 60 + 5 \\
& = & 765
\end{array}
$$

Step 1: There are not enough tens or hundreds. Rename 1 hundred to 10 tens, then rename 1 ten to 10 ones.
Step 2: Subtract the ones: 10 − 5 = 5.
Step 3: Subtract the tens: 9 − 3 = 6.
Step 4: Subtract the hundreds: 8 − 1 = 7.

There were 765 students on the trip to the ice skating rink.

600 − 283	400 − 187	500 − 266
700 − 158	900 − 356	300 − 194
800 − 277	600 − 355	100 − 37

example

Katie has 42 markers. 17 markers are pastels. Find the number of markers that are not pastels. Does the number of markers that are pastel and not pastel add up to 42?

$$
\begin{array}{r} 42 \\ -17 \\ \hline 25 \end{array}
\qquad
\begin{array}{r} 25 \\ +17 \\ \hline 42 \end{array}
$$

The number of markers that are pastel and not pastel equal 42.

Check with addition. Circle any incorrect differences.

$$
\begin{array}{r} 95 \\ -68 \\ \hline 33 \end{array}
\qquad\qquad
\begin{array}{r} 70 \\ -37 \\ \hline 33 \end{array}
\qquad\qquad
\begin{array}{r} 831 \\ -497 \\ \hline 334 \end{array}
$$

$$
\begin{array}{r} 479 \\ -283 \\ \hline 196 \end{array}
\qquad\qquad
\begin{array}{r} 559 \\ -492 \\ \hline 167 \end{array}
\qquad\qquad
\begin{array}{r} 594 \\ -265 \\ \hline 239 \end{array}
$$

Solve and check.

$$
\begin{array}{r} 83 \\ -46 \\ \hline \end{array}
\qquad\qquad
\begin{array}{r} 564 \\ -293 \\ \hline \end{array}
\qquad\qquad
\begin{array}{r} 851 \\ -697 \\ \hline \end{array}
$$

Heights of Famous Buildings	
Name of Building	Height of Building
Petronas Tower 1, Kuala Lumpur	1,483 feet
Sears Tower, Chicago	1,450 feet
Jin Mao Building, Shanghai	1,380 feet
World Trade Center, New York	1,368 feet
Empire State Building, New York	1,250 feet
Library Tower, Los Angeles	1,018 feet

How much taller than the World Trade Center is the Sears Tower?

Equation: _____

How many more feet would have to be added to the Library Tower to make it as tall as the Petronas Tower?

Equation: _____

If a 28–foot antenna were placed on top of the World Trade Center, how far would the top of the antenna be from the ground?

Equation: _____

How much shorter is the Jin Mao Building than the Empire State Building?

Equation: _____

Use the information in the chart to create and solve your own word problem.

_____

_____

_____

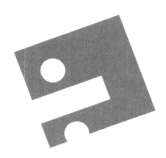

Division: Part Two

example

Nicholas arranged his 15 CD's in 3 stacks. He put the same number of CDs in each stack. How many CD's are in each stack?

3 x ? = 15

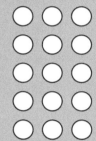

3 x 5 = 15

There are 5 CD's in each stack.

6 x _____ = 24   3 x _____ = 27   _____ x 9 = 54

_____ x 7 = 28   5 x _____ = 45   _____ x 8 = 32

9 x _____ = 9   2 x _____ = 18   5 x _____ = 0

8 x _____ = 64   _____ x 7 = 49   1 x _____ = 6

8 x _____ = 16   _____ x 5 = 45   7 x _____ = 7

example

Leroy arranged 24 chairs in 4 rows.
How many chairs are in each row?

4 x 6 = 24

24 ÷ 4 = 6

There are 6 chairs in each row.

```
X X X X X X
X X X X X X
X X X X X X
X X X X X X
```

Solve. Then write as a division equation.

4 x _____ = 32   7 x _____ = 28

_____

_____ x 9 = 72   _____ x 3 = 27

_____

6 x _____ = 42   _____ x 7 = 7

_____

5 x _____ = 40   4 x _____ = 36

_____

7 x _____ = 14   _____ x 6 = 48

_____

examples

Ana has 8 small boxes of crayons. She has 80 crayons in all. How many crayons are in each small box?

8 x 10 **= 80   or   80 ÷ 8 =** 10

There are 10 crayons in each small box.

Ho has 3 large boxes of pencils. He has a total of 300 pencils. How many pencils are in each large box?

3 x 100 **= 300   or   300 ÷ 3 =** 100

There are 100 pencils in each large box.

6 x _____ = 60   60 ÷ 6 = _____   9 x _____ = 90   90 ÷ 9 = _____

7 x _____ = 700   700 ÷ 7 = _____   _____ x 5 = 500   500 ÷ 5 = _____

_____ x 4 = 40   40 ÷ 4 = _____   _____ x 8 = 800   800 ÷ 8 = _____

600 ÷ 6 = _____   20 ÷ 2 = _____   900 ÷ 9 = _____

50 ÷ 5 = _____   70 ÷ 7 = _____   400 ÷ 4 = _____

My secret for dividing multiples of 10 and 100 is _____

_____

_____

_____

example

Mrs. Wong had 18 string beans to chop. She chopped 6 beans at a time. How many groups of beans did she chop?

Use repeated subtraction. Think: How many 6's are in 18?

```
  18
 − 6
 ────
  12
 − 6
 ────
   6
 − 6
 ────
   0
```

There are three 6's in 18.
Mrs. Wong chopped 3 groups of beans.

Use repeated subtraction.

How many 4s are in 24? _____ $40 \div 8 =$ _____ $6 \times$ _____ $= 36$

Use any method.

$45 \div 5 =$ _____ $56 \div 8 =$ _____ $48 \div 6 =$ _____

example

Jim played the same song 7 times for 21 minutes. How many minutes long is the song?

$$\begin{array}{r} 3 \\ 7\overline{)21} \end{array}$$ *Think: How many 7's are in 21?*

The song is 3 minutes long.

6 $\overline{)30}$ 5 $\overline{)40}$ 3 $\overline{)27}$

1 $\overline{)7}$ 6 $\overline{)36}$ 2 $\overline{)16}$

8 $\overline{)8}$ 7 $\overline{)28}$ 4 $\overline{)16}$

9 $\overline{)27}$ 3 $\overline{)21}$ 6 $\overline{)48}$

example

Mrs. Sanchez divided her 32 third-graders into 4 teams. How many children are on each team?

$$\begin{array}{r} 8 \\ 4 \overline{\smash{)}32} \end{array}$$

There are 8 children on each team.

$3 \overline{\smash{)}24}$ 　　　　$5 \overline{\smash{)}20}$ 　　　　$2 \overline{\smash{)}14}$

$6 \overline{\smash{)}42}$ 　　　　$7 \overline{\smash{)}14}$ 　　　　$1 \overline{\smash{)}3}$

$4 \overline{\smash{)}28}$ 　　　　$8 \overline{\smash{)}88}$ 　　　　$9 \overline{\smash{)}9}$

$6 \overline{\smash{)}0}$ 　　　　$5 \overline{\smash{)}45}$ 　　　　$3 \overline{\smash{)}30}$

$4 \overline{\smash{)}32}$ 　　　　$5 \overline{\smash{)}0}$ 　　　　$8 \overline{\smash{)}32}$

example

Jamie tried to seat 27 friends at 6 tables. She wanted the same number of friends at each table. What happened?

×　　　×　　　×　　　×　　　×　　　×

×　　　×　　　×　　　×　　　×　　　×　　　×

×　　　×　　　×　　　×　　　×　　　×　　　×

×　　　×　　　×　　　×　　　×　　　×　　　×

$$\begin{array}{r} 4\ R3 \\ 6\overline{)27} \\ -24 \\ \hline 3 \end{array}$$

Jamie seated 4 friends at each table, but 3 friends could not be seated.

Solve. You can draw X's.

$5\overline{)12}$　　　　　$8\overline{)19}$　　　　　$6\overline{)27}$　　　　　$3\overline{)29}$

$9\overline{)20}$　　　　　$2\overline{)17}$　　　　　$7\overline{)38}$　　　　　$5\overline{)39}$

example

Carlos had 9 ounces of milk to give to his cats. If he gave each cat 2 ounces of milk, how many cats were given milk?

$$
\begin{array}{r}
9 \\
-2 \\
\hline
7 \\
-2 \\
\hline
5 \\
-2 \\
\hline
3 \\
-2 \\
\hline
1
\end{array}
$$

$$
\begin{array}{r}
4\ \text{R}1 \\
2\,\overline{)\,9}
\end{array}
$$

4 cats were given milk. There was 1 ounce of milk remaining.

Use repeated subtraction to solve.

$3\,\overline{)\,23}$ $19 \div 4 = \underline{\hspace{1.5cm}}$ $7\,\overline{)\,29}$

$49 \div 9 =$ _____ $6 \times$ _____ $= 49$

$2 \overline{)19}$ _____ $\times 7 = 39$

$5 \overline{)38}$ How many 8's are in 35? _____

example

Stuart rode his horse for 12 miles. He jumped every 2 miles. How many times did he jump?

12 ÷ 2 = 6

Stuart jumped 6 times.

Lily invited 24 friends to her grandfather's camp. The same number of friends slept in each of 4 tents. How many friends slept in each tent?

Equation: _____

Olivia skated around the rink 21 times. She always stopped after going around 3 times. How many times did Olivia stop?

Equation: _____

Julian went hiking 28 times. He hiked on each of 4 different trails the same number of times. How many times did he hike on each trail?

Equation: _____

Dana entered 36 swimming races. He won every sixth race. How many races did he win?

Equation: _____

example

$29 = (7 \times q) + r$

Use any method you like to find the quotient (*q*) and the remainder (*r*).

Array	Repeated Subtraction	Multiplication Fact

Array

× × × × × × ×
× × × × × × ×
× × × × × × ×
× × × × × × ×
×

$29 = (7 \times 4) + 1$

Repeated Subtraction

29
−7
‾‾‾
22
−7
‾‾‾
15
−7
‾‾‾
8
−7
‾‾‾
1

Multiplication Fact

7 x ? = 28
7 x 4 = 28
28 + 1 = 29

$43 \div 7 =$ _____

$5 \div 2 =$ _____

$31 \div 8 =$ _____

$31 = (5 \times q) + r$

$6 \overline{)41}$

$8 \overline{)23}$

$9\overline{)38}$ $74 = (8 \times q) + r$ $5\overline{)48}$

$7\overline{)53}$ $6\overline{)36}$ $60 = (9 \times q) + r$

$7\overline{)47}$ $2\overline{)18}$ $4\overline{)31}$

There are 29 people waiting to ride the elevator. It can take 9 people at a time. How many trips will the elevator need to make?

$$29 = (9 \times q) + r$$

$$\begin{array}{r} 3R2 \\ 9\overline{\smash{)}29} \\ -27 \\ \hline 2 \end{array}$$

The elevator will need to make 3 trips with 9 people and 1 trip for the 2 remaining people. It will make 4 trips in all.

A box contains 15 dog biscuits. A dog eats
4 biscuits every day. For how many days will
the dog get his full supply of biscuits?

_____

Teddy has 37 paintings. She wants the same
number of paintings on each of 4 walls.
How many paintings will she hang on each wall?

_____

Pablo stapled 47 pieces of paper in groups of 6.
How many complete groups of paper did he staple?

_____

Genie has 37 magazines. She wants to put
them in groups of 10. How many complete
groups can she make?

_____

Zoe has 28 pet fish. She put the same number of fish in 4 different bowls. How many fish did Zoe put in each bowl?

_____

48 people are waiting for cars to take them to the picnic. Each car can hold 5 people. How many cars are needed?

_____

Jess borrowed 24 books from his grandmother. He plans to read 3 books each week. How many weeks will it take Jess to read all 24 books?

_____

Mike has 20 stamps in his collection. He puts 8 stamps on each page. How many complete pages can he fill?

_____

example

 Use any method — repeated subtraction, arrays, the algorithm, multiplication facts, or a new strategy.

$$45 = (3 \times q) + r \qquad or \qquad 45 \div 3 \qquad or \qquad 3\overline{)45}$$

The quotient is 15.

 Use any method to solve.

$56 \div 4 =$ _____ $65 \div 5 =$ _____ $6\overline{)72}$ $85 = (5 \times q) + r$

$51 \div 3 =$ _____ $153 = n \times 9$ $2\overline{)29}$ $91 = (7 \times q) + r$

Fractions

Dana and Len want to share a chocolate bar equally.
There are many ways to divide the bar into 2 equal parts.

What part of the chocolate bar does each person get?
Each person gets one half ($\frac{1}{2}$).

Shade one half ($\frac{1}{2}$).

My secret for one half ($\frac{1}{2}$) is _____

example

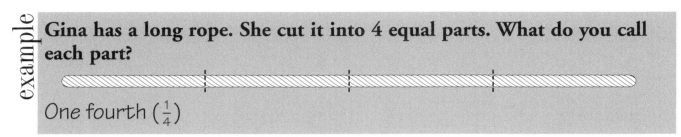

Gina has a long rope. She cut it into 4 equal parts. What do you call each part?

One fourth ($\frac{1}{4}$)

Shade one fourth ($\frac{1}{4}$).

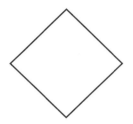

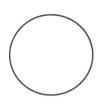

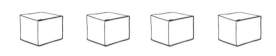

My secret for one fourth ($\frac{1}{4}$) is _____

example

What time is it?

10:00

When the minute hand is on the *12*, the time is ___ to the hour.

5:30

When the minute hand is on the *6*, it is 30 minutes past the hour.

2:15

When the minute hand is on the *3*, it is 15 minutes past the hour.

Write the time.

_____   _____   _____

FRACTIONS

_____   _____   _____

Draw hands on the clock to show the time.

8:30

3:30

10:15

6:00

4:15

2:00

example

Franklin, Teddy, Genie, and Jane are sharing a pizza equally. The pizza has 8 slices.

What do you call each slice?
one-eighth ($\frac{1}{8}$)

How many slices does each person get? 2

Shade one eighth ($\frac{1}{8}$).

Draw a picture that shows one eighth ($\frac{1}{8}$).

My secret for one eighth ($\frac{1}{8}$) is _____

example

The playing field at the school is being shared equally by 3 classes.

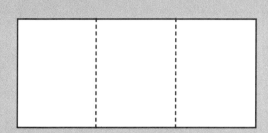

What part of the field does each class use?

Each class uses one third ($\frac{1}{3}$).

Shade one third ($\frac{1}{3}$).

My secret for one third ($\frac{1}{3}$) is _____

Write the fraction that matches the shaded part of the picture.

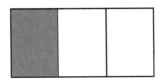

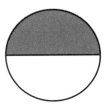

_____

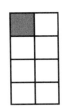

_____

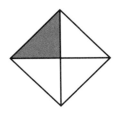

_____

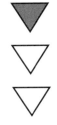

_____

example

1 gallon = 4 quarts
1 quart = 2 pints
1 pint = 2 cups
8 ounces = 1 cup

What is another name for one half of a quart?

One half of a quart means a quart is separated into 2 equal parts.

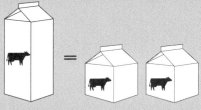

1 quart = 2 pints

Another name for one half of a quart is 1 pint.

Another name for one fourth of a gallon is _____.

Another name for one half of a pint is _____.

Another way to have 1 gallon is _____.

Another way to have one eighth of a cup is _____.

 Another name for one fourth of a quart is _____.

example

Three Ways to Write Money				
1 dollar	=	100¢	=	$1.00
1 half dollar	=	50¢	=	$.50
1 quarter	=	25¢	=	$.25
1 dime	=	10¢	=	$.10
1 nickel	=	5¢	=	$.05

School Supplies Price List	
Item	Price
eraser	$.15
pencil	$.25
notebook	$2.50
ruler	$1.10
set of markers	$3.75

Bert works at the school store. A student paid for 1 eraser with a quarter. What change should Bert give the student?

1 dime

Items Bought	Money Given to Bert	Change
1 eraser	1 quarter	
1 pencil	1 half dollar	
1 set of markers	one $5 dollar bill	
1 ruler	1 dollar and 1 quarter	
1 notebook	2 dollars and 3 quarters	
1 eraser, 1 pencil	1 half dollar	
1 notebook, 1 pencil	3 dollars	
2 pencils, 1 eraser	3 quarters	
1 of each item on the price list	one $10 dollar bill	

FRACTIONS

If you had $5.50 to spend at Bert's store, what would you buy? What change would Bert give you?

_____

_____

Write and solve your own problem using the School Supplies Price List.

_____

_____

_____

Why is 25¢ called a quarter?

_____

_____

Why is 50¢ called a half dollar?

_____

_____

example

Mrs. Scott cuts a pie into thirds.

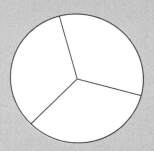

How many thirds equal 1 whole? 3

$\frac{3}{3}$ = 1 whole.

How many eighths equal 1 whole? _____

$\frac{\boxed{}}{8}$ = 1 whole

How many halves equal 1 whole? _____

$\frac{\boxed{}}{2}$ = 1 whole

Circle the fractions that are equal to 1 whole.

$\frac{5}{5}$ $\qquad$ $\frac{1}{2}$ $\qquad$ $\frac{9}{9}$ $\qquad$ $\frac{8}{8}$ $\qquad$ $\frac{5}{6}$ $\qquad$ $\frac{11}{2}$

My secret for finding the number of parts in 1 whole is _____

_____

_____

Circle the fractions that are less than 1 whole.

$$\frac{3}{4} \qquad \frac{1}{4} \qquad \frac{3}{3} \qquad \frac{2}{5} \qquad \frac{10}{12} \qquad \frac{4}{4}$$

My secret for knowing that a fraction is less than 1 whole is _____

_____

_____

Circle the fractions that are greater than 1 whole.

$$\frac{5}{2} \qquad \frac{3}{8} \qquad \frac{4}{5} \qquad \frac{6}{6} \qquad \frac{1}{9} \qquad \frac{8}{3}$$

My secret for knowing if a fraction is greater than 1 whole is _____

_____

_____

example

Which is greater—one half ($\frac{1}{2}$) of a cookie or one fourth ($\frac{1}{4}$) of a cookie?

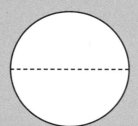 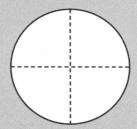

If a cookie is cut into 2 equal parts, the parts are larger than if the cookie is cut into 4 equal parts.

$\frac{1}{2}$ > $\frac{1}{4}$

Write >, <, or = to compare the fractions. Use fraction pieces for help.

$\frac{1}{2}$ _____ $\frac{1}{8}$ 　　　　$\frac{1}{6}$ _____ $\frac{1}{3}$ 　　　　$\frac{1}{4}$ _____ $\frac{1}{2}$

$\frac{1}{5}$ _____ $\frac{1}{2}$ 　　　　$\frac{1}{1000}$ _____ $\frac{1}{4}$ 　　　　$\frac{1}{9}$ _____ $\frac{1}{50}$

$\frac{1}{2}$ _____ $\frac{1}{2}$ 　　　　$\frac{5}{5}$ _____ $\frac{1}{2}$ 　　　　$\frac{2}{7}$ _____ $\frac{7}{7}$

$\frac{3}{8}$ _____ 1 whole 　　　$\frac{12}{12}$ _____ 1 whole 　　　$\frac{4}{8}$ _____ $\frac{1}{2}$

My secret for comparing fractions is _____

_____

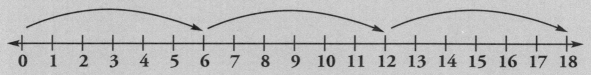

Sam walked 18 blocks on Monday. He walked one-third ($\frac{1}{3}$) of that distance on Tuesday. How far did he walk on Tuesday?

When you separate 18 blocks into 3 equal parts, there are 6 blocks in each part.

Sam walked 6 blocks on Tuesday.

Jesse drank one half of a quart of water.
How many pints of water did Jesse drink?

_____

Gina practiced the piano until 5:00. Then she practiced for one half hour longer. What time did Gina finish practicing?

_____

Toby cut the slice of toast into fourths. Then she ate half of the toast. How many fourths did Toby eat?

_____

Tim biked 7 miles. This was one half of the distance that Maska biked. How many miles did Maska bike?

_____

Since Isabel made a web page, 12 friends have looked
at it. Yesterday, one third of them saw it. How
many of her friends saw the web page yesterday?

_____

Dominic swam for one half an hour on Monday
and one fourth of an hour on Tuesday. On which
day did he swim for a longer time? How much longer?

_____

 Pearl read one fourth of a book on Friday
and one half of it on Saturday. Did she finish
the book? If not, how much more of the book is
left to read?

_____

Measurement

What kinds of things are measured?

_____

_____

_____

_____

Name something that can be measured by the standard unit.

inch _____

month _____

hour _____

pound _____

dollar _____

quart _____

degree _____

example

What is the length of the line?

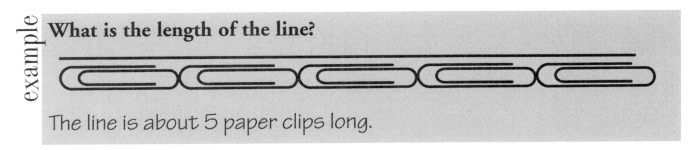

The line is about 5 paper clips long.

Measure the length of the line.

Use a crayon as the unit of measure.

The line is about _____ crayons long.

Use your pencil as the unit of measure.

The line is about _____ pencils long.

Use an eraser as the unit of measure.

This line is about _____ erasers long.

Find 3 things in the room that have length. Choose a unit of measure such as string, straws, handspans, pencils, or footsteps to measure each.

What I Measured	Unit I Used	Number of Units

example

The standard units for length are inch, foot, yard, and mile.

12 inches (in.) = 1 foot (ft)

3 feet = 1 yard (yd)

5,280 feet = 1 mile (mi)

The line is 1 inch long.

Find 3 things in the room that can be measured in inches.

Measure them.

What I Measured	Number of Inches

Find 3 things in the room that can be measured in feet.

Measure them.

What I Measured	Number of Feet

Complete each table.

X (Number of Feet)	Y (Number of Inches)
1	12
2	
3	
4	
	120
	72

X (Number of Yards)	Y (Number of Feet)
1	3
2	
3	
4	
5	
6	

X (Number of Inches)	Y (Number of Yards)
36	1
72	
108	
144	

X (Number of Feet and Inches)	Y (Number of Inches)
4 ft 3 in.	51 in.
2 ft 5 in.	
3 ft 11 in.	
1 ft. 9 in.	

What day is today? _____

What month is it? _____

What year is it? _____

Complete the calendar for a month that has 30 days.

Sunday	Monday	Tuesday	Wednesday	Thursday	Friday	Saturday
		1	2			

Use the calendar you made to answer each question.

The third Thursday of the month is Tanya's birthday. What is the date of Tanya's

birthday? _____

Tennis is one week after the 5th. On what day is tennis? _____

What is the last day of the month? _____

On what day is the 21st? _____

What is the first day of the month? _____

Complete the table.

X (Number of Weeks)	Y (Number of Days)
0	0
1	7
2	
3	
4	
5	
6	
7	

How many years old are you? _____

 How many months old are you? _____

 How many weeks old are you? _____

example

What time is it?

10:25

It takes the minute hand 5 minutes to move from one number to the next.

Write the time.

_____

_____

_____

_____

_____

_____

_____

_____

_____

Draw hands on the clock to show the time.

7:00

11:30

3:55

How much time is there between 11:30 and 12:10? _____

It is 4:20. What time will it be in 3 hours? _____

It is 5:15. What time will it be in $4\frac{1}{2}$ hours? _____

A TV program is 1-hour long. It ends at 8:30. What time does it begin? _____

Complete the table.

X (Number of Minutes)	Y (Number of Hours)
60	1
120	2
	3
	4
300	

X (Number of Hours)	Y (Number of Days)
24	1
48	2
	3
	4
	5

example

16 ounces (oz) = 1 pound (lb)   **2,000 pounds = 1 ton (T)**

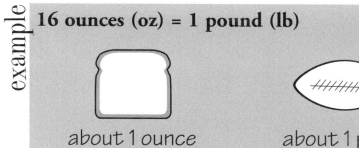

about 1 ounce   about 1 pound   about 1 ton

Name 3 items in the classroom that can be weighed using ounces.

_____

_____

Name 3 items in the classroom that can be weighed using pounds.

_____

_____

Complete the table.

X (Number of Pounds)	Y (Number of Ounces)
1	16
2	
3	
4	

X (Number of Tons)	Y (Number of Pounds)
1	2,000
2	
3	
4	

example

1 dollar
$1.00
100¢

half dollar
$.50
50¢

quarter
$.25
25¢

dime
$.10
100¢

nickel
$.05
5¢

penny
$.01
1¢

Write the value of the bills and coins.

_____

_____

What coins will make the amount?

18¢ _____

$.92 _____

$.36 _____

Complete the table.

Dollars	Dimes	Pennies	Value
8	4	6	$8.46
6	2	7	
			$2.69
9	5		$9.53

Write >,<, or = to compare amounts of money.

$7.03 _____ $7 and 3 dimes   86¢ _____ 7 dimes and 18 pennies

$.48 _____ 4 dimes and 8 pennies $9.05 _____ 7 dollars and 20 dimes

Solve.

$9.56	$8.72	$52.09	$3.96
+ 5.34	+ 1.09	− 1.26	− 2.89

$4.68	$58.81	$3.40	$61.04
− 1.77	+ 7.09	−1.68	−20.16

Find out how much change you should receive.

You buy lunch for $2.85 and pay with a 5-dollar bill. _____

You buy a drink for 68¢ and pay with a 1-dollar bill. _____

example

Liquid Measures

8 ounces = 1 cup
2 cups = 1 pint
2 pints = 1 quart
4 quarts = 1 gallon

ounce   **cup**   **pint**   **quart**   **gallon**

Write in order from least to greatest: cup, ounce, gallon, quart, pint.

_____

What are 3 different ways to make a quart?

_____

_____

_____

Which holds more: a pint container that is filled with water or a pint container that is filled with juice? Explain your secret.

_____

_____

_____

MEASUREMENT

Write >, <, or = to compare.

2 cups _____ 1 quart   3 pints _____ 2 cups

4 pints _____ 1 gallon   4 quarts _____ 1 gallon

8 ounces _____ 1 pint   2 quarts _____ 5 pints

Complete the table.

P (Number of Pints)	Q (Number of Quarts)
2	1
4	
6	
8	
10	

C (Number of Cups)	P (Number of Pints)
4	2
8	
12	

What is your secret for changing units of capacity?

_____

_____

_____

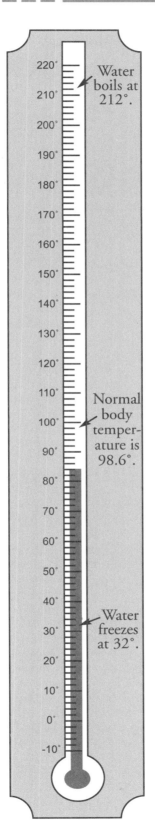

example

Temperature is a measure of how hot or cold something is. A thermometer measures temperature in degrees (°).
As the temperature gets warmer, the liquid in the tube goes up. As the temperature gets cooler, the liquid goes down.
The thermometer shows 84°.

What would you wear outdoors if the temperature was 25°?

_____

What would you wear outdoors if the temperature was 83°?

_____

If the temperature goes from 20° to 50°, does it get warmer

or cooler?

_____

If the temperature goes from 58° to 44°, does it get warmer

or cooler?

_____

example

Metric units are used all over the world. They are based on the place value of tens.

Meter is used for length.
Liter is used for capacity.
Gram is used for weight.

about 1 meter long   about 2 liters full   about 1 gram in weight

Name two things that can be measured with each unit.

meter _____

liter _____

gram _____

Name the unit that you would use for measuring the following.

how tall you are _____

how much you weigh _____

how much juice you drank _____

example

Kilo- means 1,000.

1 kilometer = 1,000 meters

Centi- means one hundredth.

1 centimeter = $\frac{1}{100}$ of a meter or 100 centimeters = 1 meter

1 kiloliter = _____ liters   _____ kilogram = 1,000 grams

_____ centigrams = 1 gram   100 centiliters = _____ liter

Here are the prefixes that are used with metric units.

kilo-	hecto-	deka-	UNIT	deci-	centi-	milli-
1,000	100	10	1	$\frac{1}{10}$	$\frac{1}{100}$	$\frac{1}{1000}$

What is your secret for prefixes and metric units?

_____

_____

_____

_____

Geometry

example

A point is an exact location.

•

A curve is a set of points that form a path.

A line is a straight curve. A line segment is part of a line.

This is an angle.

Write *P* for point, *C* for curve, *L* for line, and *A* for angle.

•

_____   _____   _____

_____   _____   _____

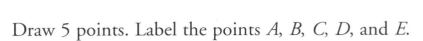

Draw 5 points. Label the points *A*, *B*, *C*, *D*, and *E*.

Draw 5 different curves.

Draw 5 different lines.

Draw 5 different angles.

example

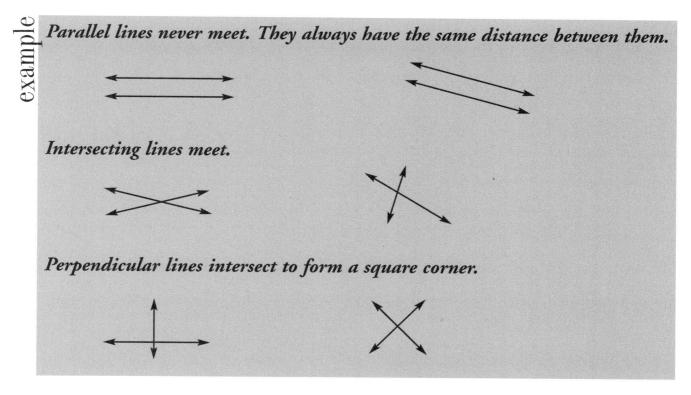

Parallel lines never meet. They always have the same distance between them.

Intersecting lines meet.

Perpendicular lines intersect to form a square corner.

Write *parallel*, *intersecting*, or *perpendicular* for each pair of lines. If the lines are perpendicular, you do not also have to write *intersecting*.

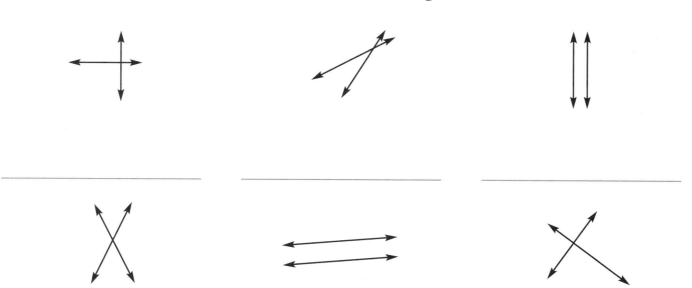

Draw a pair of parallel lines.

Draw a pair of intersecting lines.

Draw a pair of perpendicular lines.

example

Simple Closed Curves.

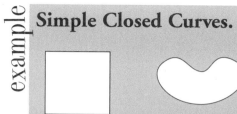

Curves That Are Not Simple.

 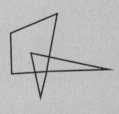 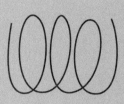

Draw a ring around the simple closed curves.

   **3**

My 2 secrets for simple closed curves are _____

_____

_____

Draw 4 curves that are simple closed curves.

Draw 1 curve that is simple but not closed.

Draw 3 curves that are not simple.

example

A polygon is a simple closed curve made up of 3 or more line segments.

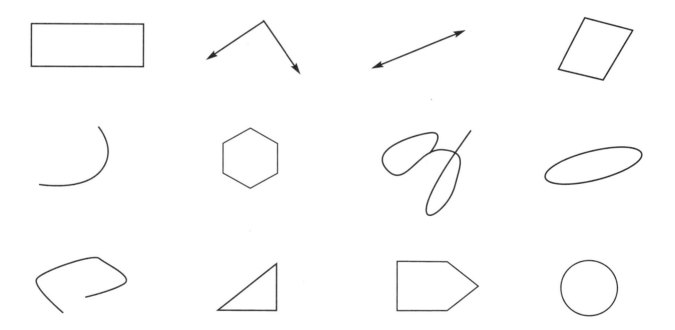

| triangle | quadrilateral | pentagon | hexagon | octagon |

Draw a ring around each polygon.

Draw 4 different triangles.

Draw 6 different quadrilaterals.

Draw 3 more polygons.

Draw 2 figures that are not polygons.

example

Perimeter is the distance around a figure. Which figure has the greater perimeter?.

Use a piece of string for the unit of measure.

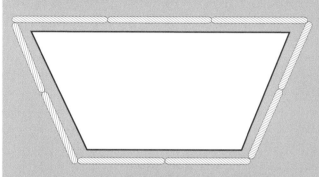

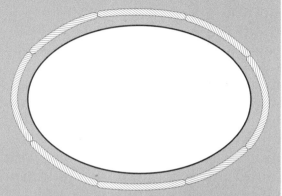

The perimeter of the quadrilateral is 9 pieces of string.

The perimeter of the simple closed curve is 8 pieces of string.

The quadrilateral has the greater perimeter.

Find the perimeter of each figure. Choose a unit of measure and mark where each unit ends.

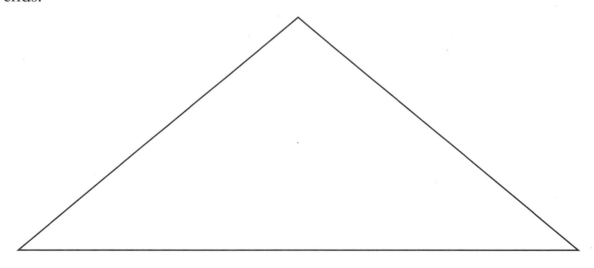

The unit of measure is _____. The perimeter is _____.

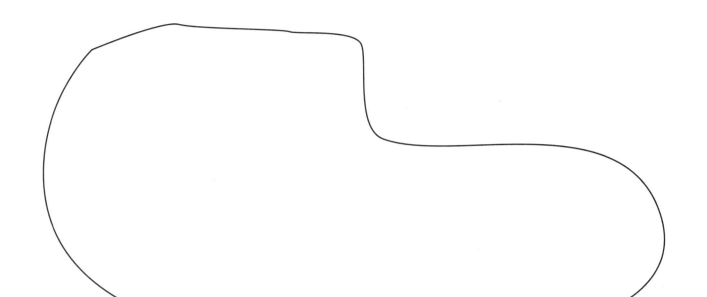

The unit of measure is _____.   The perimeter is _____.

Use the same unit of measure to find the perimeter of each figure.

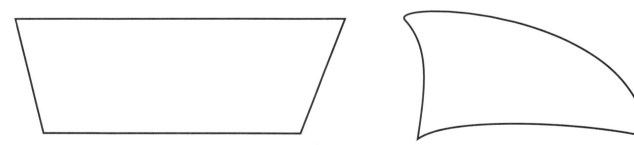

The unit of measure is _____.

The perimeter of the quadrilateral is _____.

The perimeter of the curve is _____.

The _____ has the greater perimeter.

184

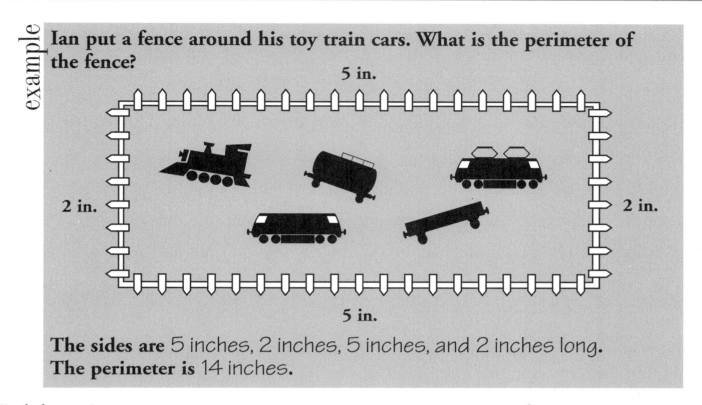

example

Ian put a fence around his toy train cars. What is the perimeter of the fence?

5 in.

2 in.   2 in.

5 in.

The sides are 5 inches, 2 inches, 5 inches, and 2 inches long.
The perimeter is 14 inches.

Find the perimeter.

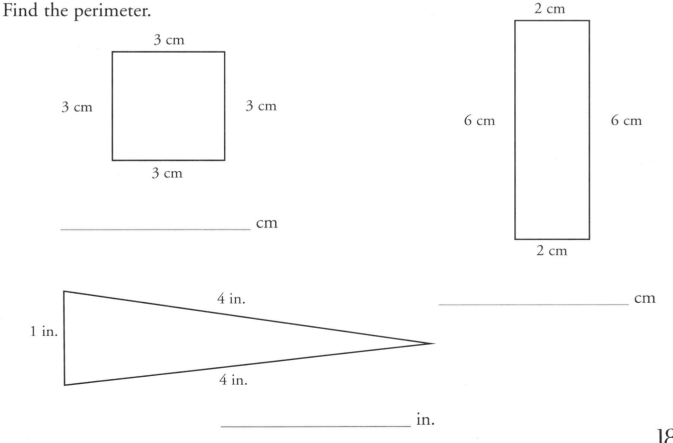

3 cm

3 cm   3 cm

3 cm

_____ cm

2 cm

6 cm   6 cm

2 cm

_____ cm

4 in.

1 in.

4 in.

_____ in.

Measure the sides using centimeters. Find the perimeter.

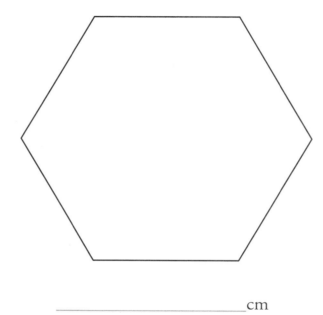

_____cm

Create your own figure. Find the perimeter.

_____

example

John wants to cover his yard with squares of grass. About how many squares does he need?

The number of units needed to cover a figure is the area of the figure.

Unit of Measure

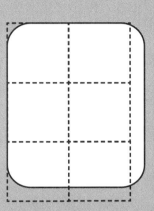

John needs about 6 squares.

About how many units cover each figure?

Unit of measure:

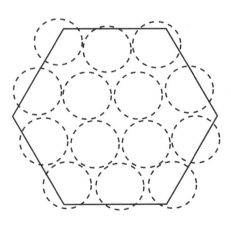

about _____ units

187

Unit of measure:

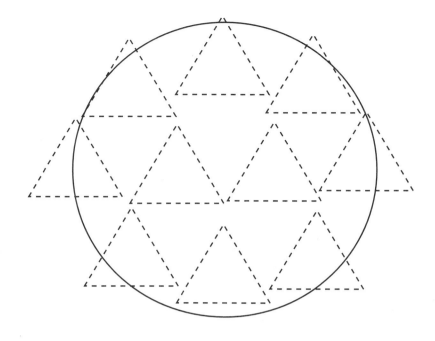

about _____ units

Draw your own figure. Decide on a unit of measure. Trace the unit within your figure. Estimate the area.

Unit of measure:

about _____ units

The center of the circle is point *C.*

A radius is a line segment that has one endpoint on the circle and one endpoint on the center of the circle.

A diameter is a line segment that goes through the center of the circle and has its two endpoints on the circle.

Draw a point in the center of the circle.
Draw a radius.
Draw a diameter.

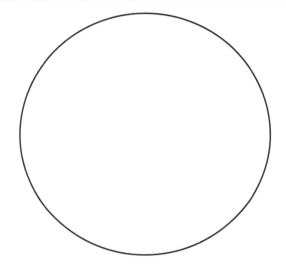

Color each diameter orange.
Color each radius green.
Mark the center of the circle purple.

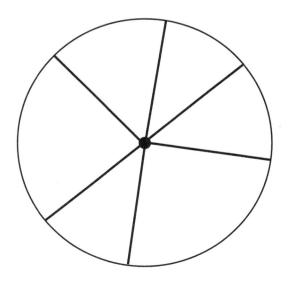

examples

These are solid figures.

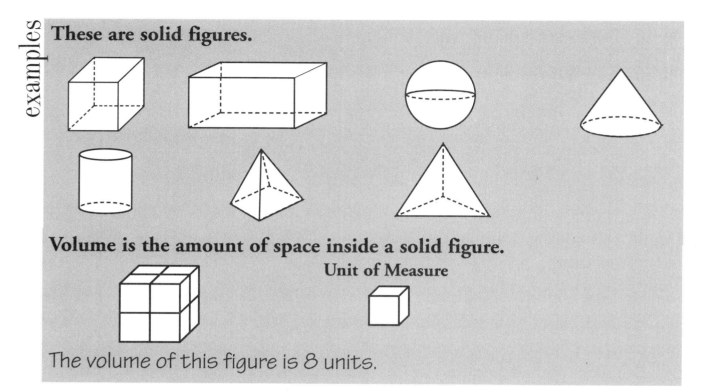

Volume is the amount of space inside a solid figure.

Unit of Measure

The volume of this figure is 8 units.

Ring the solid figures.

 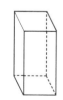 

Find the volume of each solid figure.

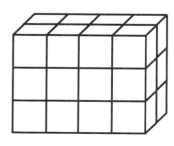

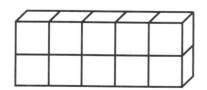

190

_____ units   _____ units

A figure has symmetry if it can be divided into two matching parts.

Draw a ring around the figures that have symmetry.

 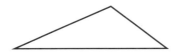

Draw a line of symmetry on each figure.

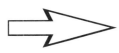 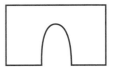

 **10**

Draw a figure that has symmetry. Draw the line of symmetry.

Draw a figure that does not have symmetry.

This is your chance to be creative with geometry. Use the ideas in this chapter in a creative way. Here are some suggestions.

- Draw a picture using geometric shapes.
- Write a story about a sad circle and a happy square.
- Write about where you have seen geometric figures—at home, in school, in your neighborhood.
- Do an investigation. Try to find out more about one of the lessons.

Whatever you do, . . . BE CREATIVE!

Organizing Information

example

15 students wrote their favorite color on cards.

blue	purple	blue	red	yellow
purple	black	black	blue	green
green	red	purple	white	purple

They organized the data on a chart. Which color has the most votes?

Favorite Colors	
Colors	**Number of Votes**
black	2
blue	3
green	2
purple	4
red	2
white	1
yellow	1

Purple has the most votes.

Which colors have the fewest votes? _____

Which colors have the same number of votes as black? _____

Which color has 3 votes? _____

Some students voted for their favorite sports.

| hockey | softball | skating | hockey | biking | hockey |
| biking | skating | hockey | soccer | skating | soccer |

Organize the data on a chart.

What is the most popular sport? _____

What is the least popular sport? _____

What sport would you add to the chart? _____

Choose your own topic and organize your data in a chart on a separate piece of paper.

example

In which month are the most birthdays?

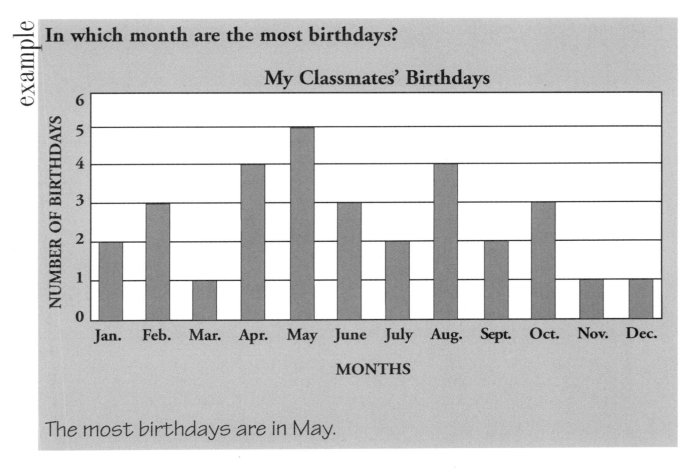

The most birthdays are in May.

Which months have 2 birthdays?

_____

In which months are the fewest birthdays?

_____

What other comparisons can you make from the bar graph? _____

_____

Create your own bar graph.

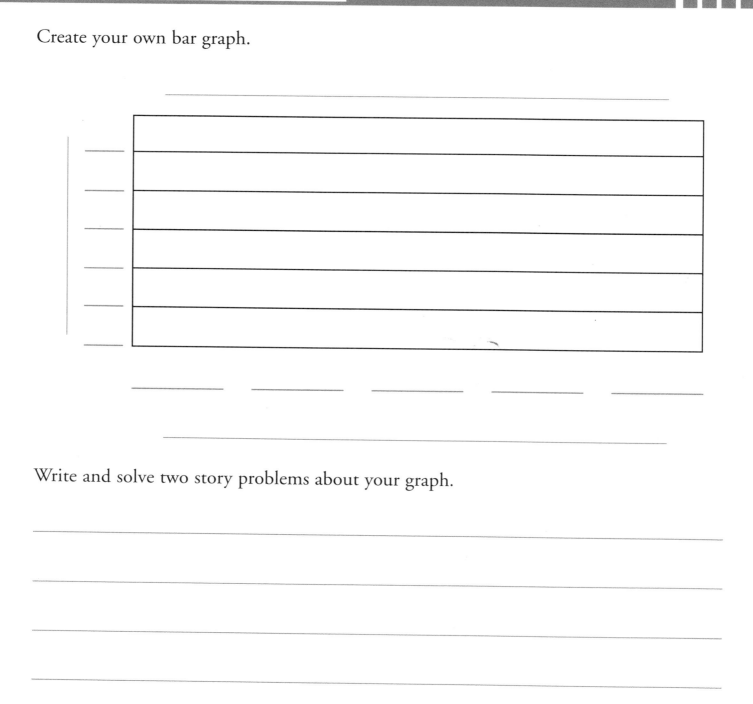

Write and solve two story problems about your graph.

example

How many students are in third grade?

Number of Students in Grades 1-3

First Grade	☺ ☺ ☺ ☺ ☺ ☺ ☺ ☺
Second Grade	☺ ☺ ☺ ☺ ☺ ☺ ☺
Third Grade	☺ ☺ ☺ ☺ ☺ ☺ ☺ ☺

Key: ☺ = 4 students

There are 30 students in third grade.

Which grade has the most students? _____

How many students are in that grade? _____

How many students are in second grade? _____

How many students are in all three grades? _____

How many more students are in first grade than in third grade? _____

Create your own pictograph.

Key: _____

Explain what your pictograph shows.

_____

_____

_____

_____

example

The circle graph shows how Ruby spends her day. Does she spend more time sleeping or eating?

Ruby's Day

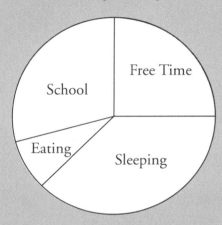

Ruby spends more time sleeping.

Does Ruby spend more time in school or free time?

_____

What does Ruby spend the least amount of time doing?

_____

What does Ruby spend the most amount of time doing?

_____

203

Elisa spent $6 for a movie ticket, $2.50 for a snack, and $1.50 for a magazine. Write each item in the correct place on the circle graph.

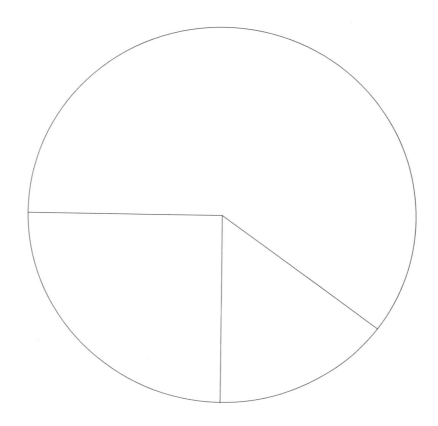

How much money did Elisa spend? _____

Make your own creative graph. It may be a combination of the graphs that you have studied: bar graphs, pictographs, and circle graphs, or it may be entirely your own design. Go creative!

What is the title of your graph? _____

List your data.

_____

_____

_____

_____

Make your graph.